Picture
Maze
Mania

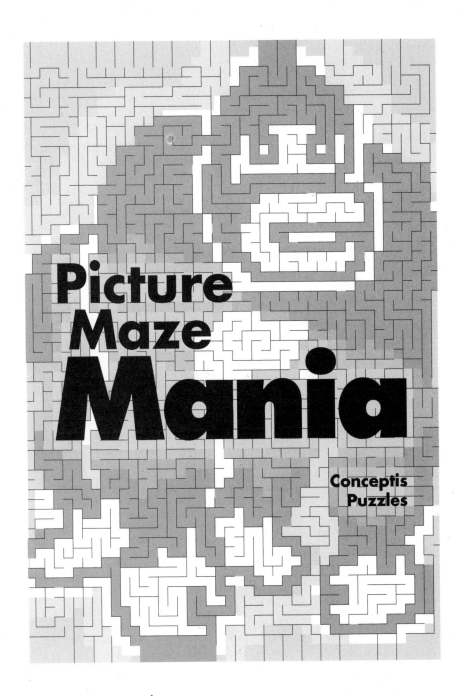

Picture Maze Mania

Conceptis Puzzles

STERLING INNOVATION
An imprint of Sterling Publishing Co., Inc.

New York / London
www.sterlingpublishing.com

STERLING, and the distinctive Sterling logo,
STERLING INNOVATION and the Sterling Innovation logo
are registered trademarks of Sterling Publishing Co., Inc.

2   4   6   8   10   9   7   5   3   1

Published by Sterling Publishing Co., Inc.
387 Park Avenue South, New York, NY 10016
© 2009 by Sterling Publishing Co., Inc.

Puzzles in this book previously appeared in *Picture That! Mazes*,
Super Hidden Picture Mazes, *Perplexing Picture Mazes*, and *Mysterious Picture Mazes*
Copyright © 2006 and 2007 by Conceptis Puzzles

Distributed in Canada by Sterling Publishing
c/o Canadian Manda Group, 165 Dufferin Street
Toronto, Ontario, Canada M6K 3H6
Distributed in the United Kingdom by GMC Distribution Services
Castle Place, 166 High Street, Lewes, East Sussex, England BN7 1XU
Distributed in Australia by Capricorn Link (Australia) Pty. Ltd.
P.O. Box 704, Windsor, NSW 2756, Australia

Manufactured in the United States of America
All rights reserved

Sterling ISBN 978-1-4027-6450-9

For information about custom editions, special sales, premium and
corporate purchases, please contact Sterling Special Sales
Department at 800-805-5489 or specialsales@sterlingpublishing.com.

CONTENTS

Introduction

Solve a maze and create a picture! There are two types of picture maze puzzles in this book, basic and reversed. To start out, solve each of these fun puzzles just as you would a traditional maze: find the true path by starting at the maze's entrance and drawing a line to the maze's exit, avoiding incorrect paths and dead ends.

But the fun is not over once you exit! What's next? In the basic kind of maze, you color in the path you traced with a dark, thick line of pen or marker to create a picture. In the other kind, which we call the reversed maze (labeled R), after you have traced the true path lightly in pencil, color in all the incorrect paths with a think pen or pencil to create your picture.

You might be surprised to learn that picture mazes of this kind were invented in Japan over 20 years ago. Today picture mazes have a dedicated following among children and adults all over the world. By reversing the tones of the maze paths, we can creat more detailed pictures than are possible with basic picture mazes alone, as well as recognizable portrait mazes. So grab your marker and pencil and get started!

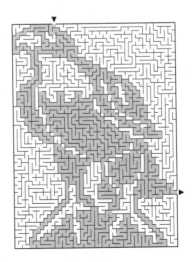

Maze #1

Maze #2

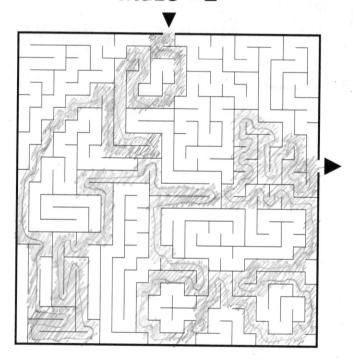

Solutions on page 302

Maze #3

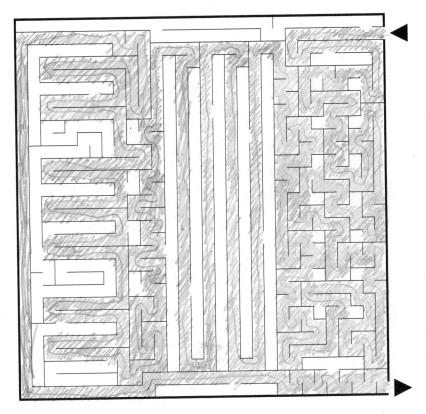

Solution on page 302

Maze #4

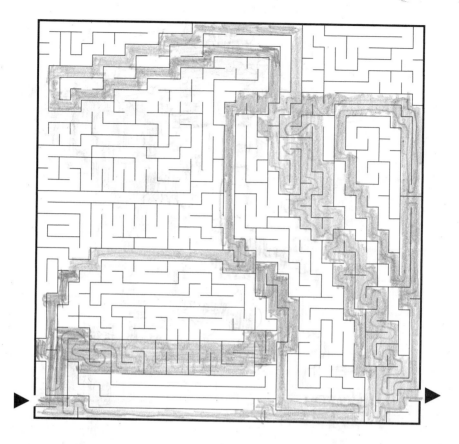

Solution on page 302

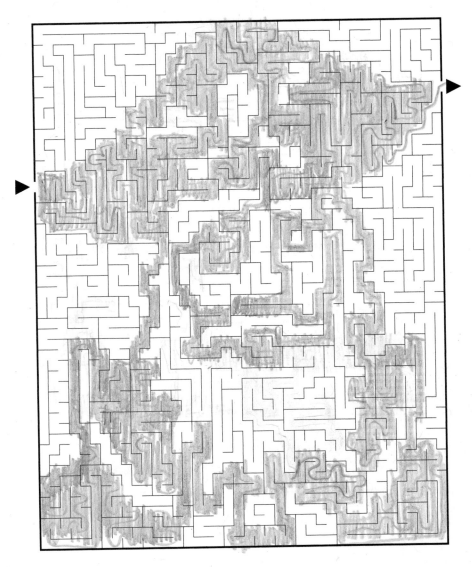

Solution on page 303

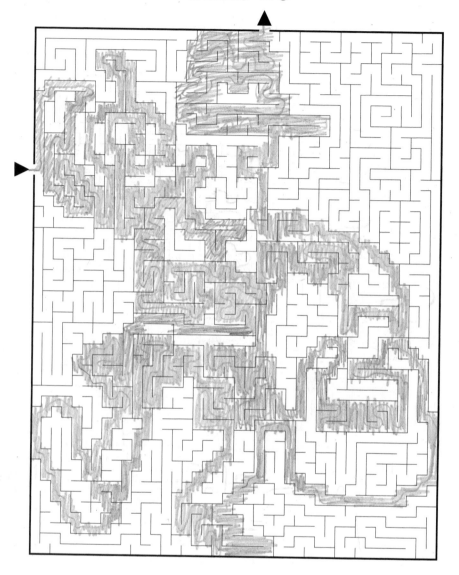

Solution on page 303

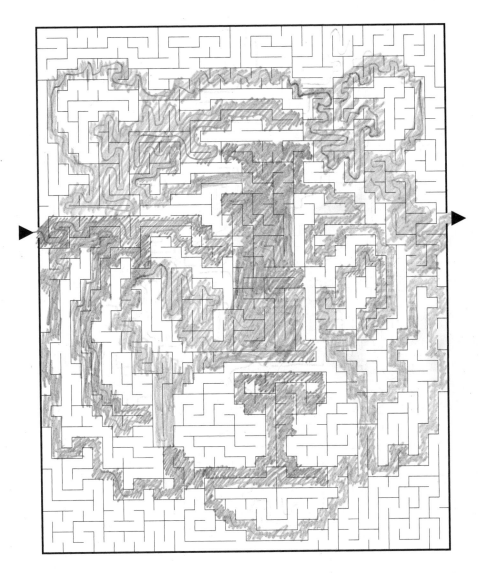

Solution on page 303

Solution on page 303

Maze #9

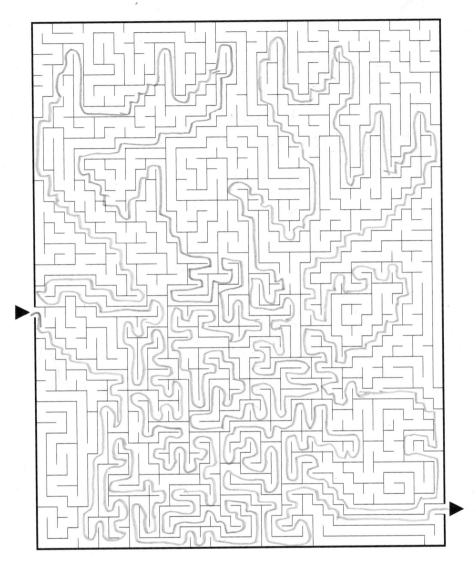

Solution on page 304

Solution on page 304

Solution on page 304

Solution on page 304

Maze #13

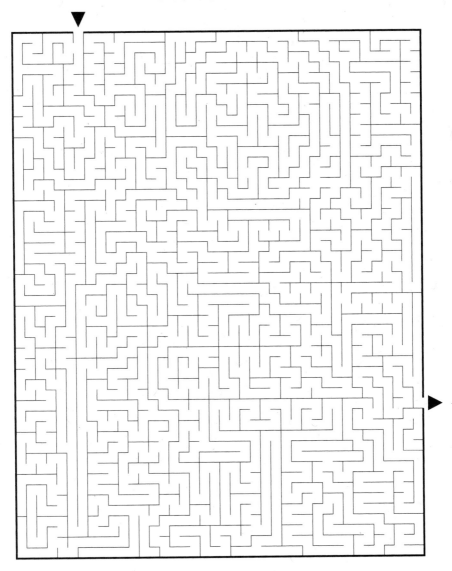

Solution on page 305

Solution on page 305

Maze #15

Solution on page 305

Solution on page 306

Maze #17

Solution on page 306

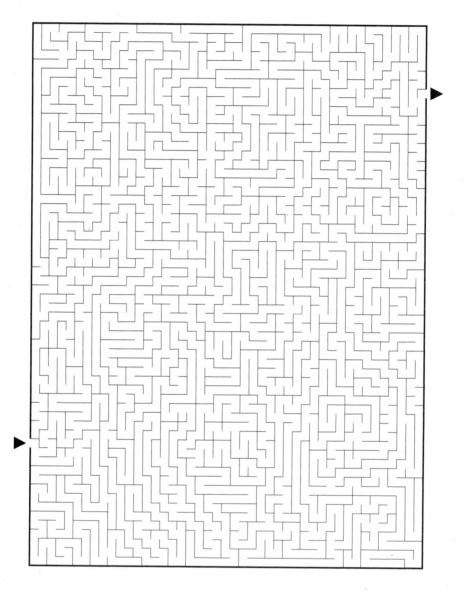

Solution on page 306

Maze #19

Solution on page 307

Solution on page 307

Maze #21

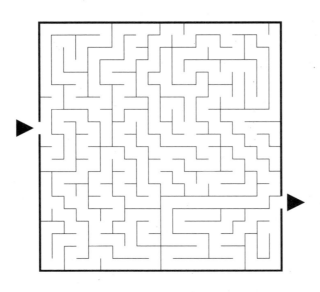

Maze #22

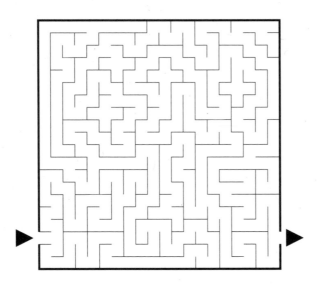

Solutions on page 307

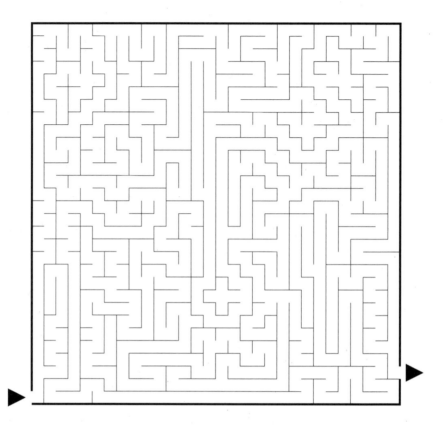

Solution on page 308

Maze #24

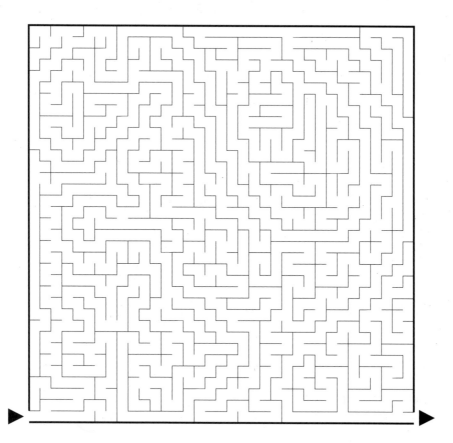

Solution on page 308

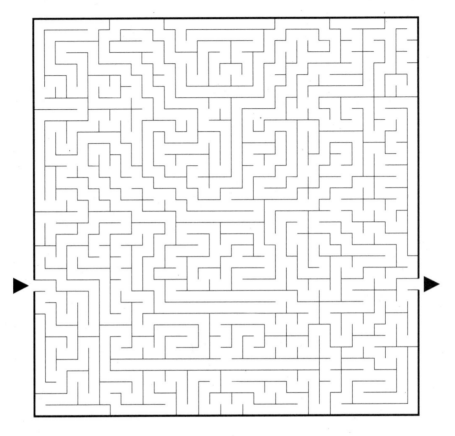

Solution on page 308

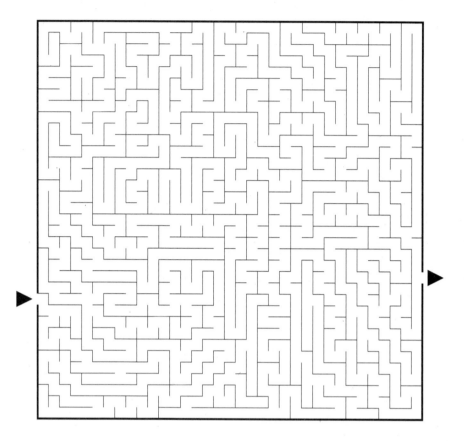

Solution on page 308

Solution on page 309

Solution on page 309

Solution on page 309

Solution on page 310

Solution on page 310

Solution on page 310

Solution on page 311

Solution on page 311

Solution on page 311

Maze #36

Solution on page 312

Solution on page 312

Solution on page 312

Solution on page 312

Maze #40

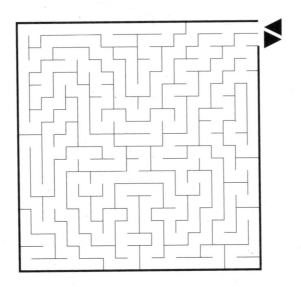

Maze #41

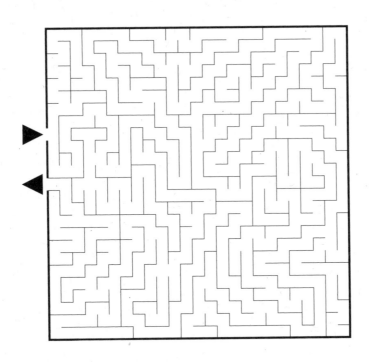

Solutions on page 313

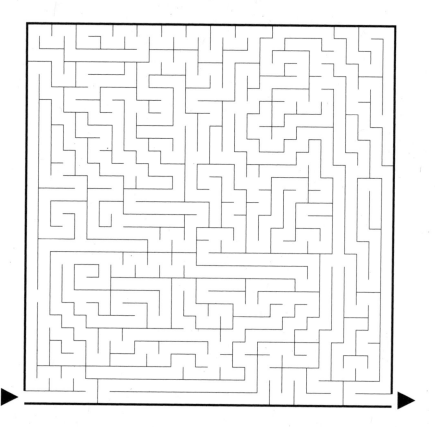

Solution on page 313

Solution on page 313

Solution on page 314

Maze #45

Solution on page 314

Maze #46

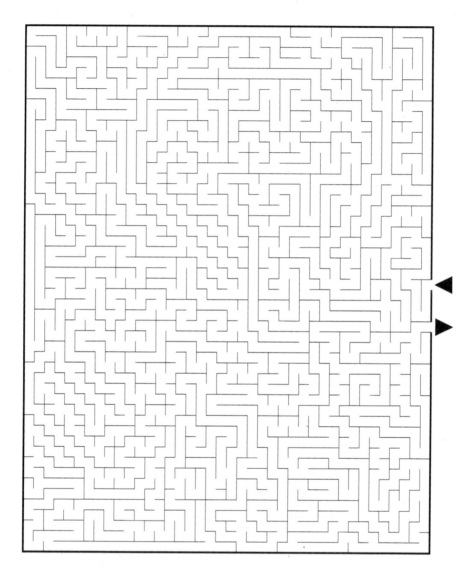

Solution on page 314

Solution on page 314

Solution on page 315

Solution on page 315

Solution on page 315

Maze #51

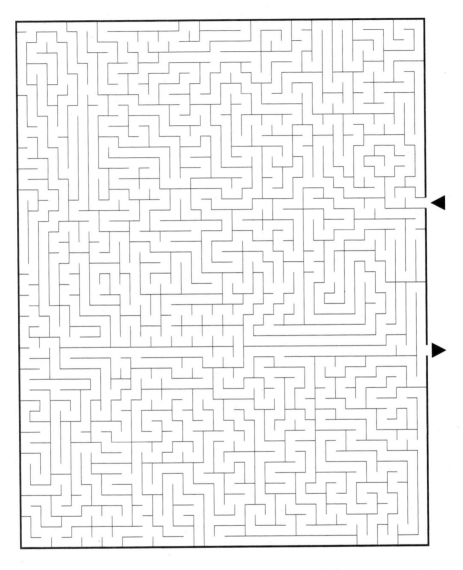

Solution on page 316

Maze #52

Solution on page 316

Maze #53

Solution on page 316

Solution on page 317

Solution on page 317

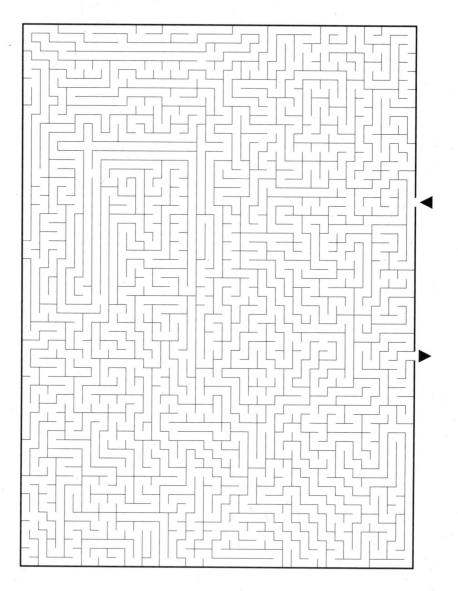

Solution on page 317

Maze #57

Solution on page 318

Solution on page 318

Maze #59

Solution on page 318

Solution on page 319

Maze #61

Solution on page 319

Solution on page 319

Solution on page 320

Solution on page 320

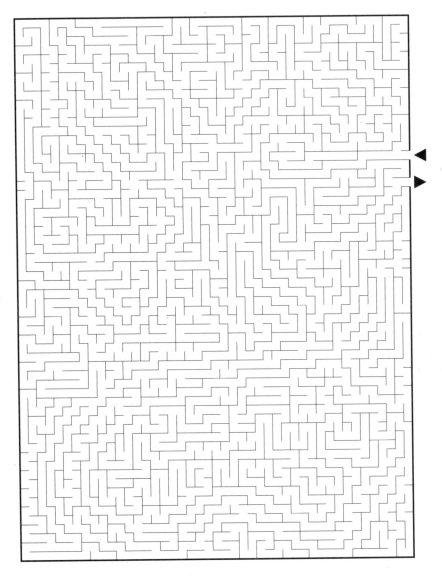

Solution on page 320

Maze #66

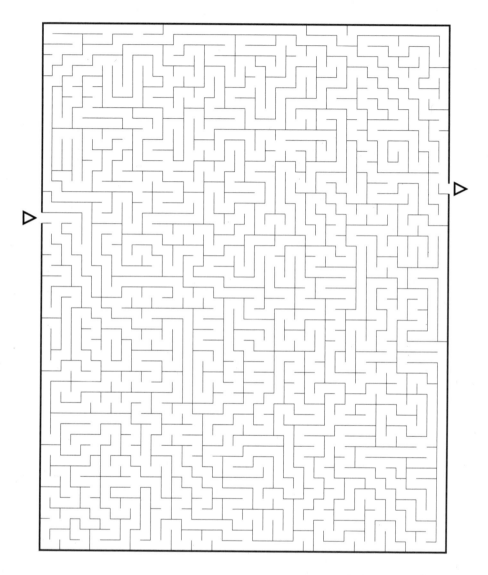

Solution on page 321

R This is a reversed maze. After you have traced the true path (solution) lightly in pencil, color in all the wrong paths with a thick pen or pencil to create your picture.

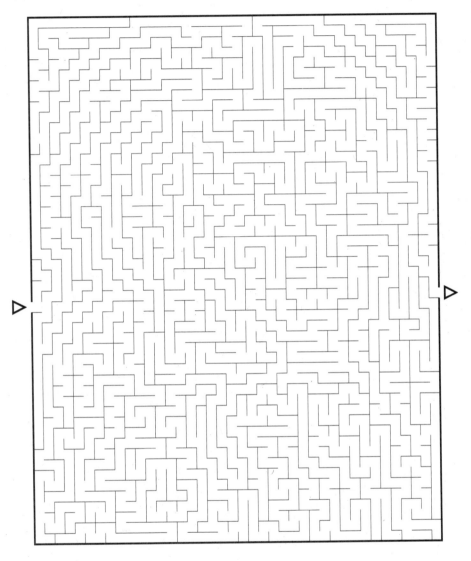

Solution on page 321

R This is a reversed maze. After you have traced the true path (solution) lightly in pencil, color in all the wrong paths with a thick pen or pencil to create your picture.

Solution on page 321

R This is a reversed maze. After you have traced the true path (solution) lightly in pencil, color in all the wrong paths with a thick pen or pencil to create your picture.

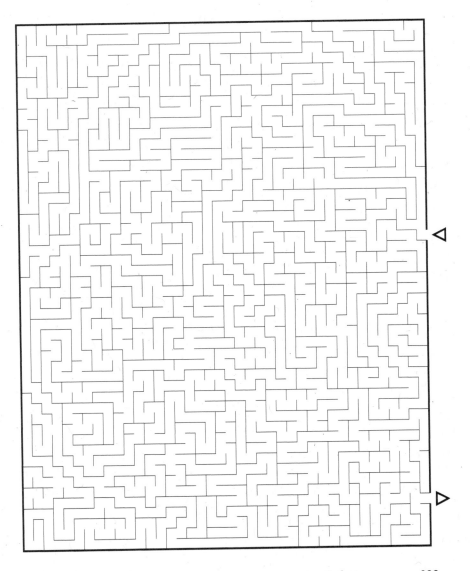

Solution on page 322

R This is a reversed maze. After you have traced the true path (solution) lightly in pencil, color in all the wrong paths with a thick pen or pencil to create your picture.

Solution on page 322

R This is a reversed maze. After you have traced the true path (solution) lightly in pencil, color in all the wrong paths with a thick pen or pencil to create your picture.

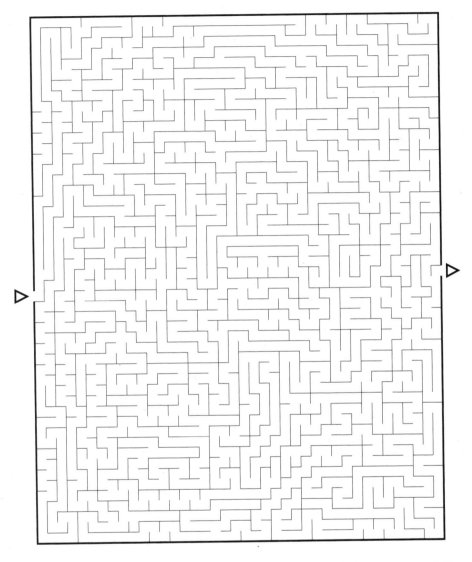

Solution on page 322

R This is a reversed maze. After you have traced the true path (solution) lightly in pencil, color in all the wrong paths with a thick pen or pencil to create your picture.

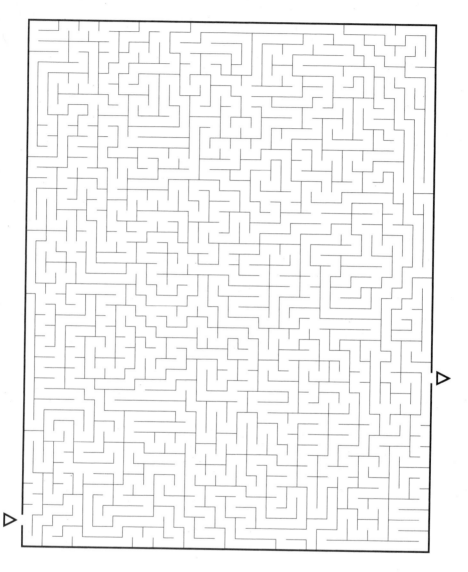

Solution on page 322

R This is a reversed maze. After you have traced the true path (solution) lightly in pencil, color in all the wrong paths with a thick pen or pencil to create your picture.

Maze #73

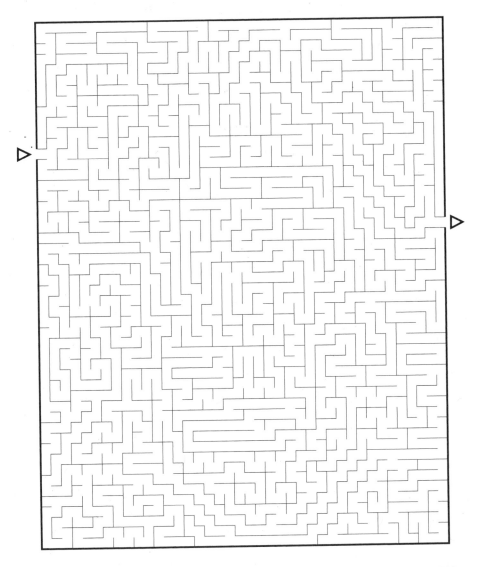

Solution on page 323

R This is a reversed maze. After you have traced the true path (solution) lightly in pencil, color in all the wrong paths with a thick pen or pencil to create your picture.

Solution on page 323

R This is a reversed maze. After you have traced the true path (solution) lightly in pencil, color in all the wrong paths with a thick pen or pencil to create your picture.

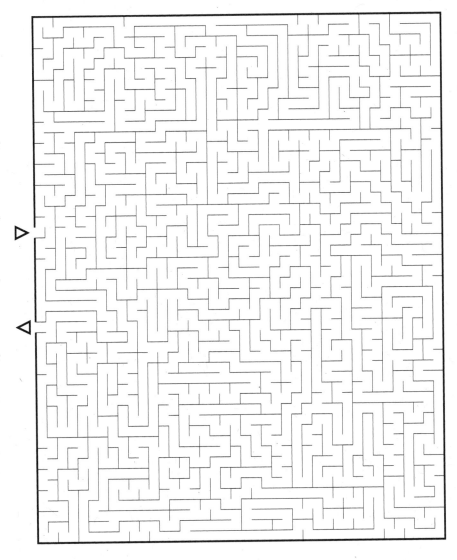

Solution on page 323

R This is a reversed maze. After you have traced the true path (solution) lightly in pencil, color in all the wrong paths with a thick pen or pencil to create your picture.

Maze #76

Solution on page 323

R This is a reversed maze. After you have traced the true path (solution) lightly in pencil, color in all the wrong paths with a thick pen or pencil to create your picture.

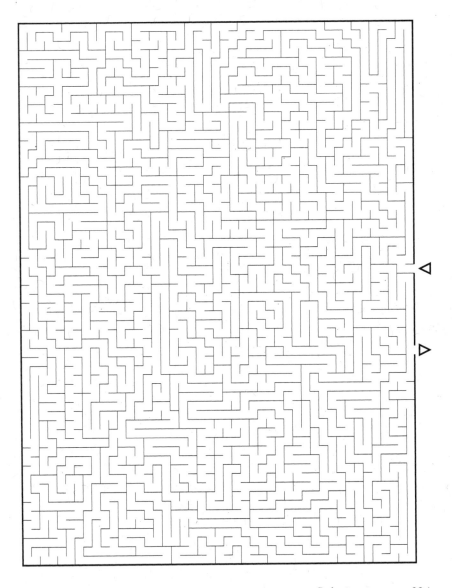

Solution on page 324

R This is a reversed maze. After you have traced the true path (solution) lightly in pencil, color in all the wrong paths with a thick pen or pencil to create your picture.

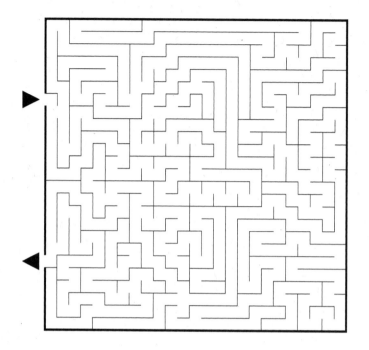

Solution on page 324

Maze #79

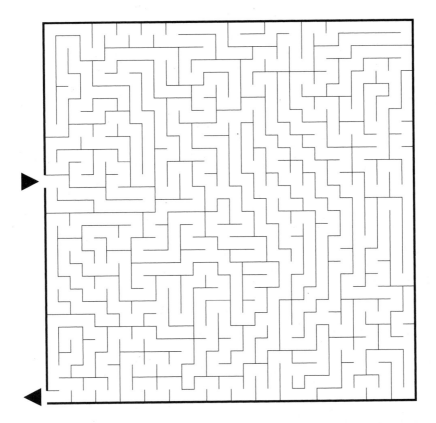

Solution on page 324

Maze #80

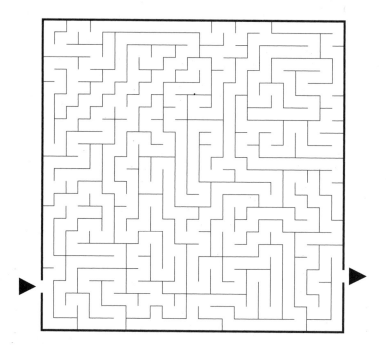

Maze #81

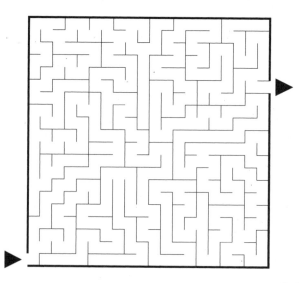

Solutions on page 324

Maze #82

Maze #83

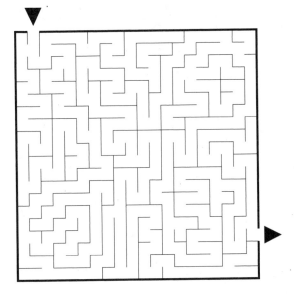

*Solutions on
page 325*

Maze #84

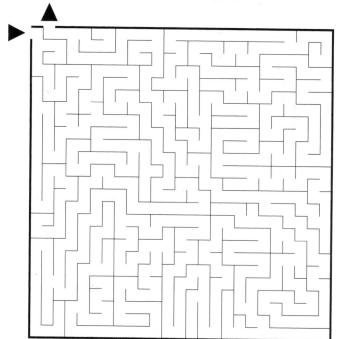

Maze #85

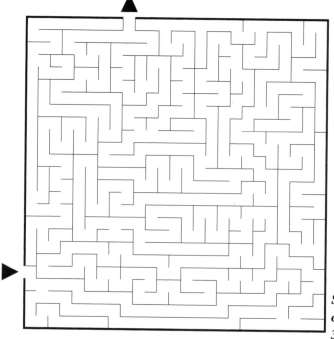

Solutions on page 325

Maze #86

Maze #87

Solutions on page 326

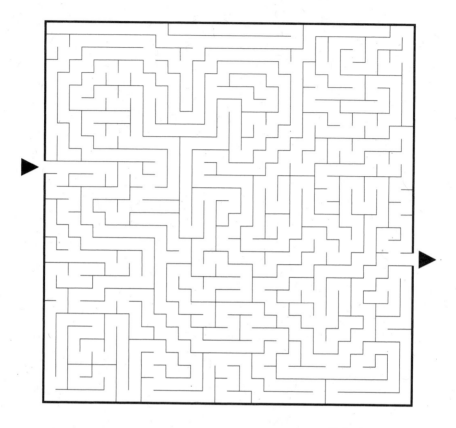

Solution on page 326

Maze #89

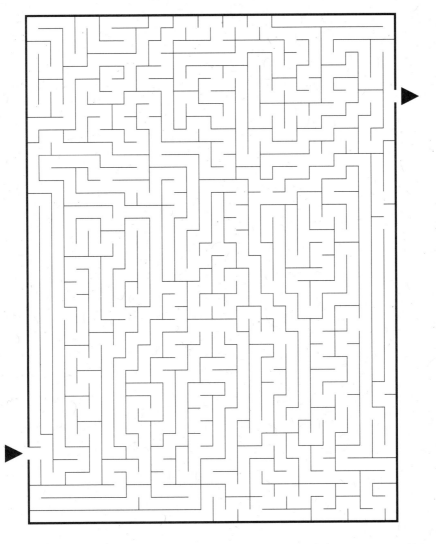

Solution on page 326

Solution on page 327

Solution on page 327

Maze #92

Solution on page 327

Maze #93

Solution on page 327

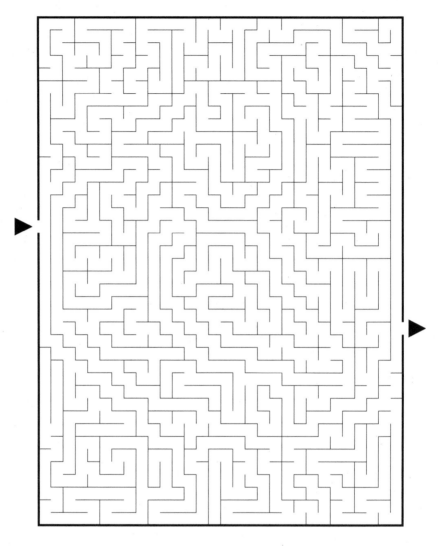

Solution on page 328

Solution on page 328

Solution on page 328

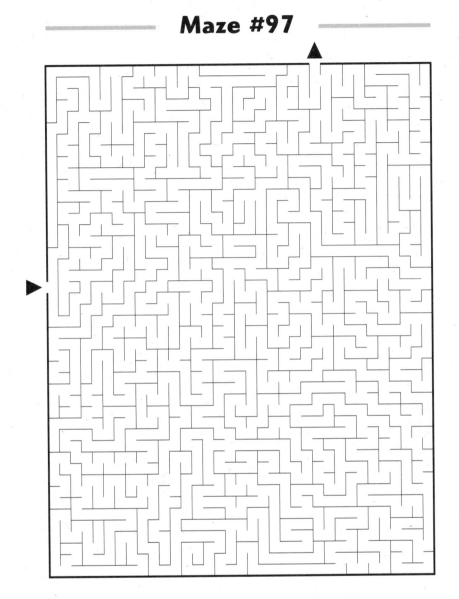

Solution on page 328

Maze #98

Solution on page 328

Solution on page 329

Solution on page 329

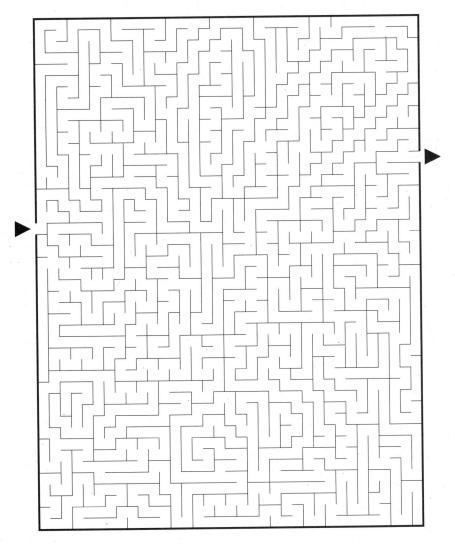

Solution on page 329

Solution on page 329

Solution on page 330

Solution on page 330

Solution on page 330

Solution on page 330

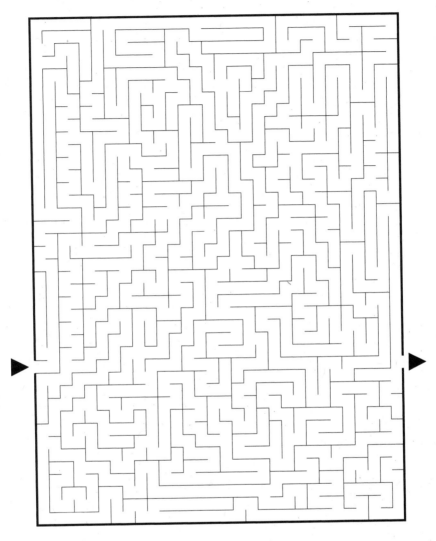

Solution on page 331

Solution on page 331

Solution on page 331

Solution on page 331

Solution on page 332

Solution on page 332

Maze #113

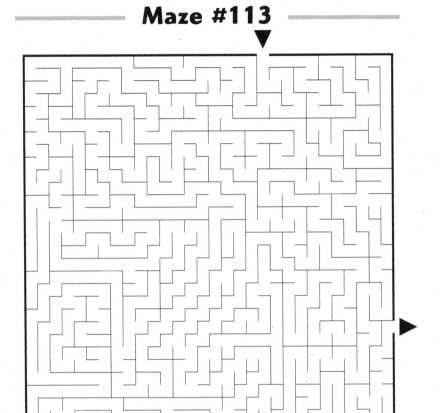

Solution on page 332

Solution on page 332

Solution on page 333

Solution on page 333

Solution on page 333

Solution on page 333

Solution on page 334

Solution on page 334

Solution on page 334

Maze #122

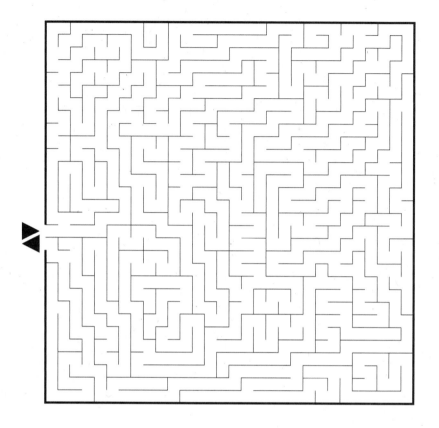

Solution on page 334

Maze #123

Solution on page 334

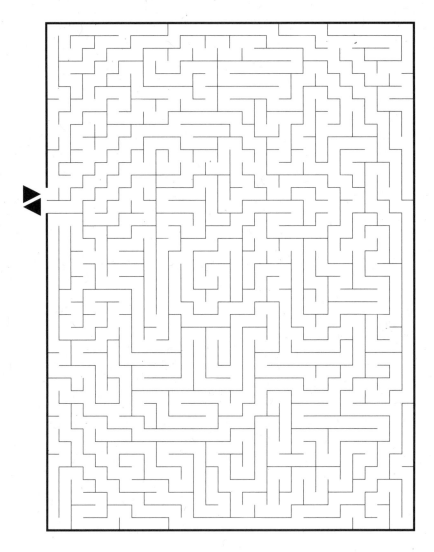

Solution on page 335

Solution on page 335

Solution on page 335

Solution on page 335

Solution on page 336

Solution on page 336

Solution on page 336

Solution on page 336

Solution on page 336

Maze #133

Solution on page 337

Solution on page 337

Solution on page 337

Solution on page 337

Maze #137

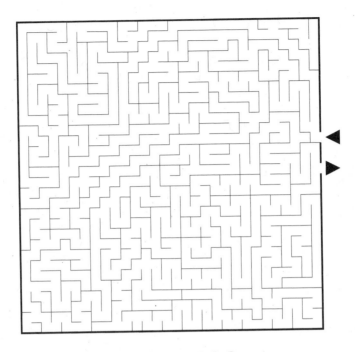

Maze #138

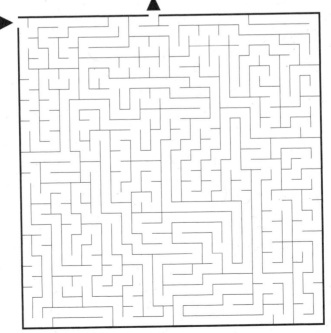

Solutions on page 337

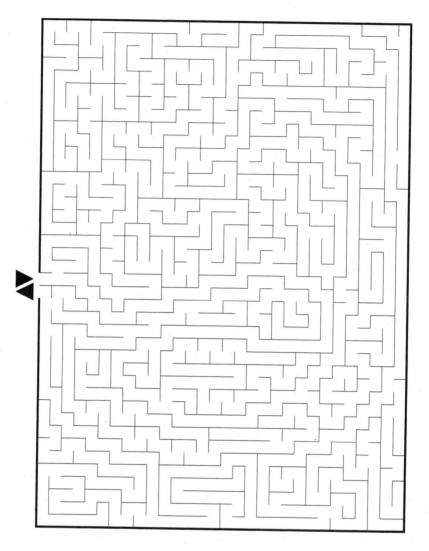

Solution on page 338

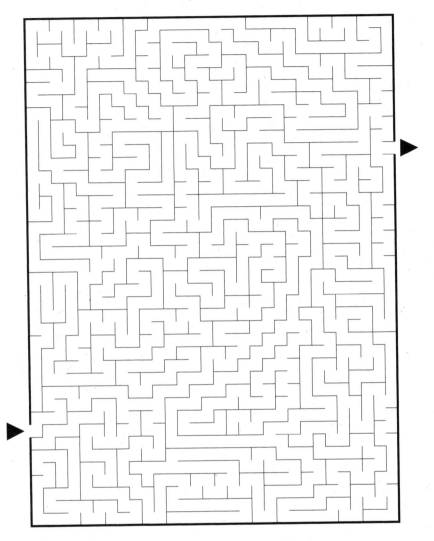

Solution on page 338

Solution on page 338

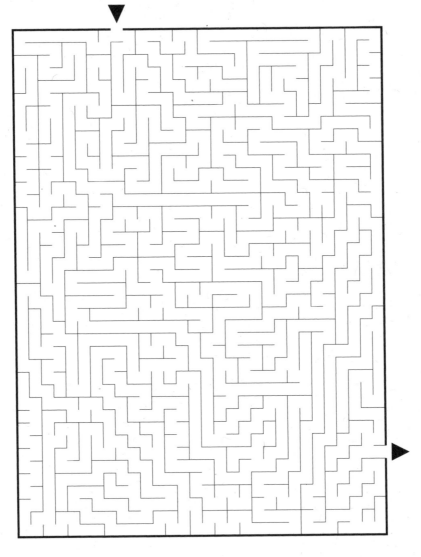

Solution on page 339

Maze #143

Solution on page 339

Maze #144

Solution on page 339

Maze #145

Solution on page 340

Solution on page 340

Maze #147

Solution on page 340

Solution on page 341

Maze #149

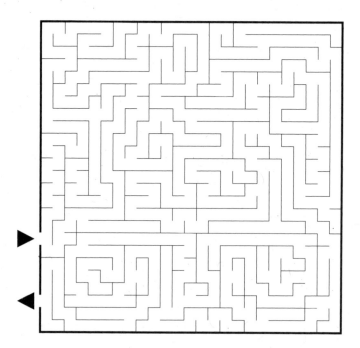

Maze #150

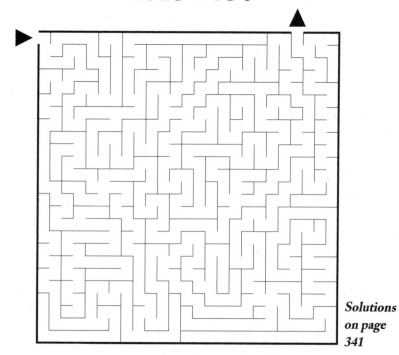

Solutions on page 341

Maze #151

Solution on page 342

Solution on page 342

Solution on page 342

Maze #154

Solution on page 343

Solution on page 343

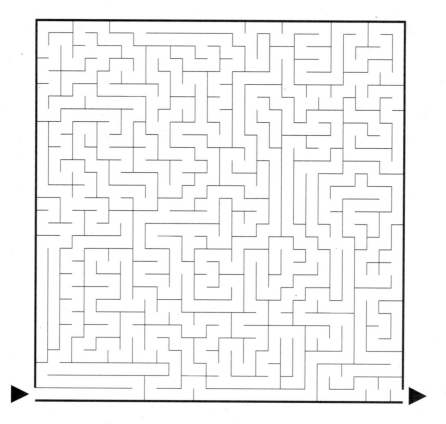

Solution on page 343

Maze #157

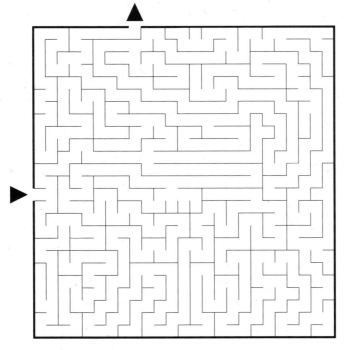

Maze #158

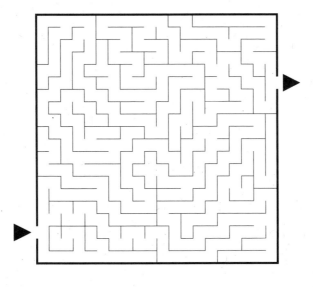

*Solutions
on page
343*

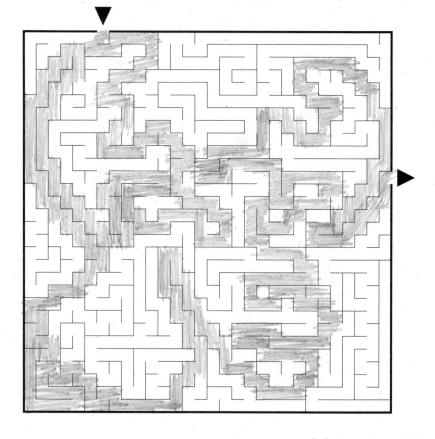

Solution on page 344

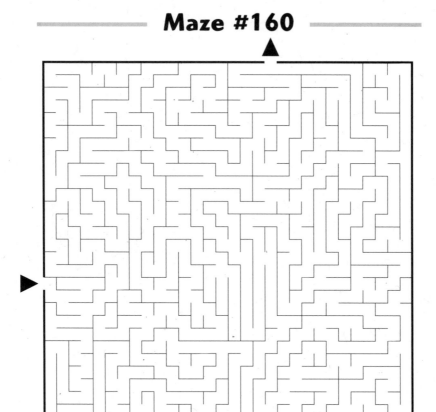

Solution on page 344

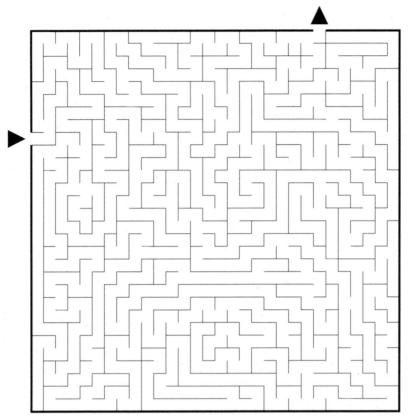

Solution on page 344

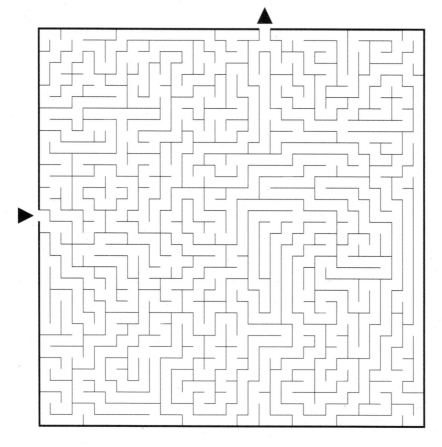

Solution on page 344

Maze #163

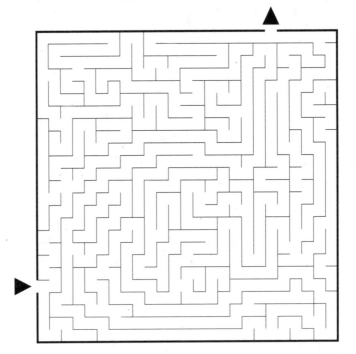

Maze #164

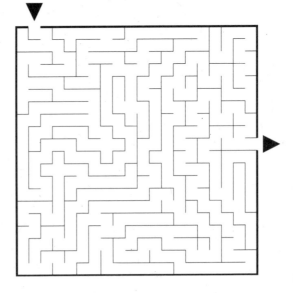

Solutions on page 344

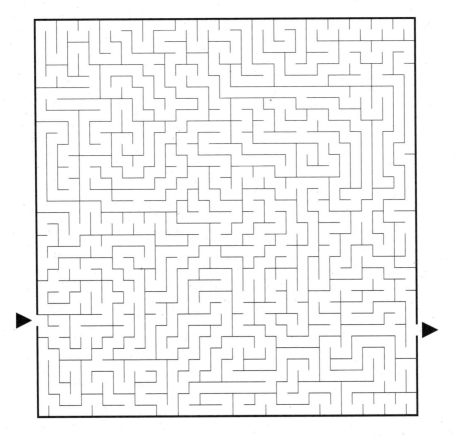

Solution on page 345

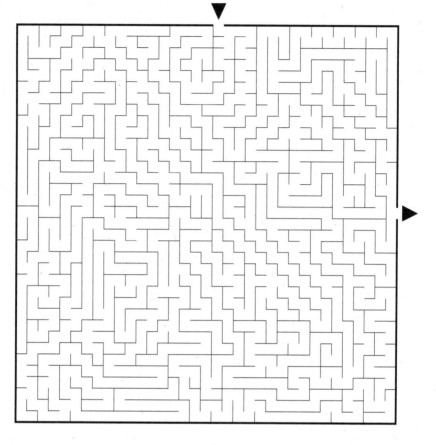

Solution on page 345

Solution on page 345

Solution on page 346

Solution on page 346

Solution on page 346

Solution on page 346

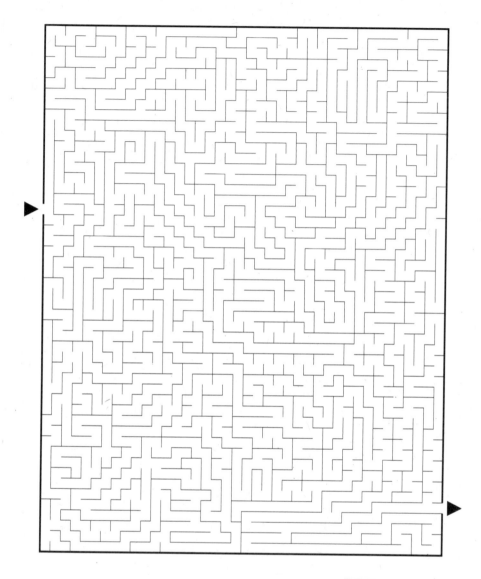

Solution on page 347

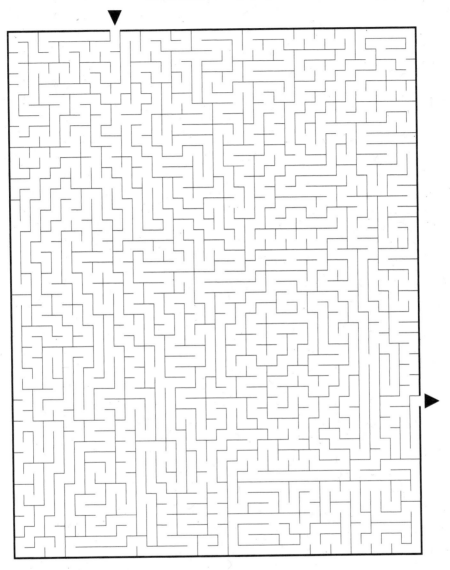

Solution on page 347

Maze #174

Solution on page 347

Solution on page 347

Solution on page 348

Solution on page 348

Solution on page 348

Solution on page 348

Solution on page 349

Solution on page 349

Solution on page 349

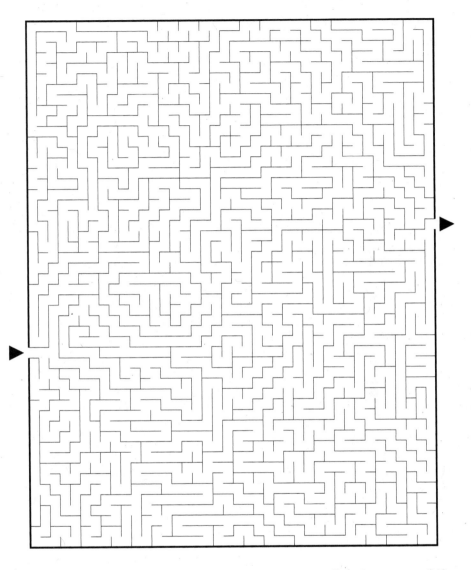

Solution on page 349

Solution on page 350

Solution on page 350

Solution on page 350

Solution on page 350

Maze #188

Solution on page 351

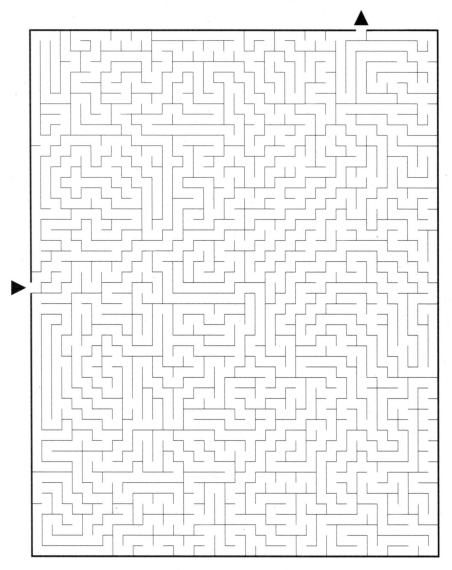

Solution on page 351

Solution on page 351

Maze #191

Solution on page 351

Solution on page 352

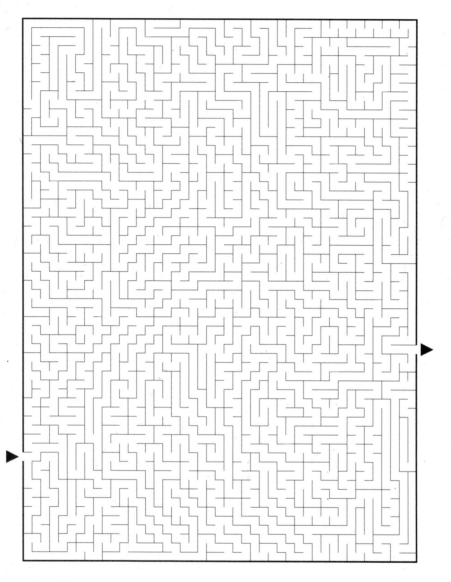

Solution on page 352

Solution on page 352

Solution on page 352

Maze #196

Solution on page 353

Maze #197

Solution on page 353

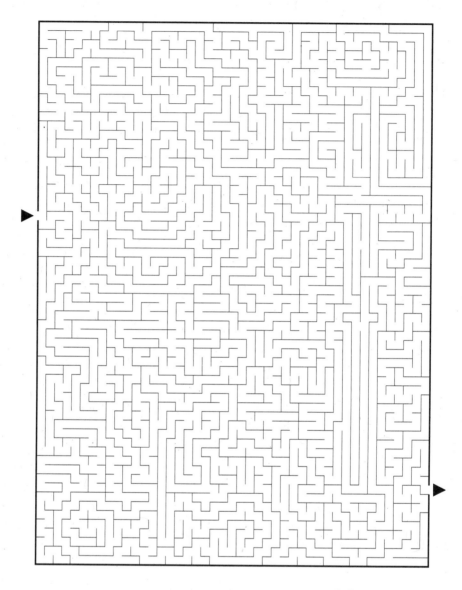

Solution on page 353

Solution on page 353

Solution on page 354

Solution on page 354

Solution on page 354

Solution on page 354

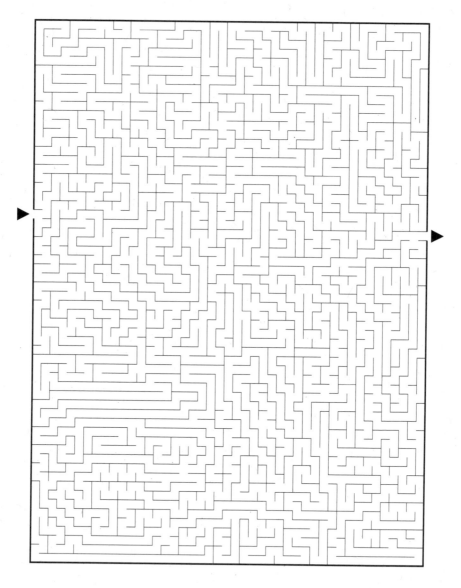

Solution on page 355

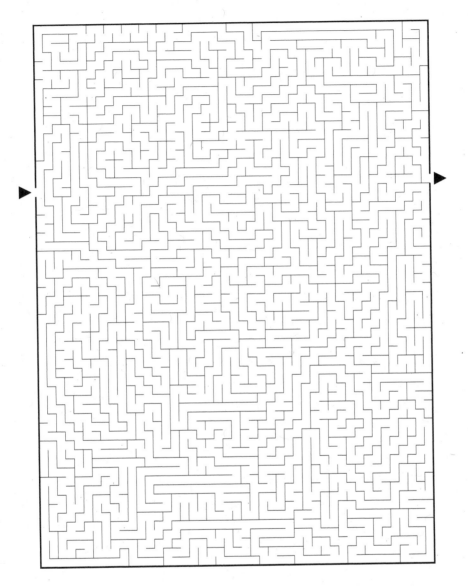

Solution on page 355

Maze #206

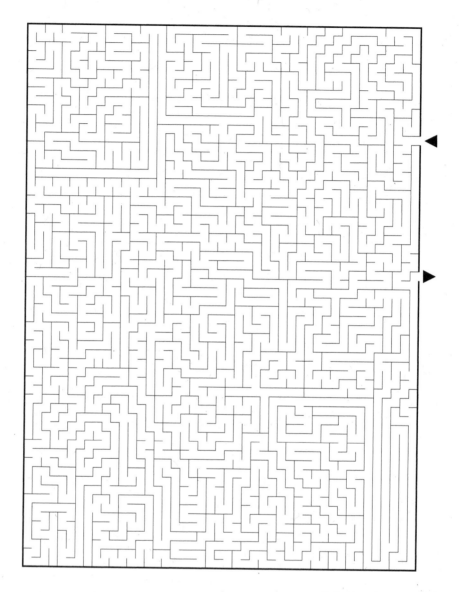

Solution on page 355

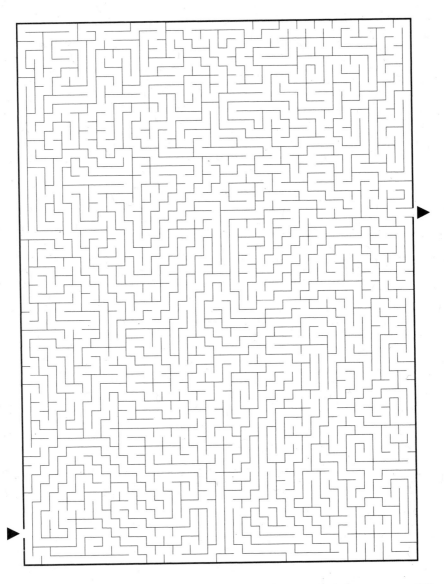

Solution on page 355

Solution on page 356

Solution on page 356

Solution on page 356

Solution on page 356

Solution on page 357

Maze #213

Solution on page 357

Maze #214

Solution on page 357

Maze #215

Solution on page 357

Solution on page 358

Solution on page 358

Maze #218

Solution on page 358

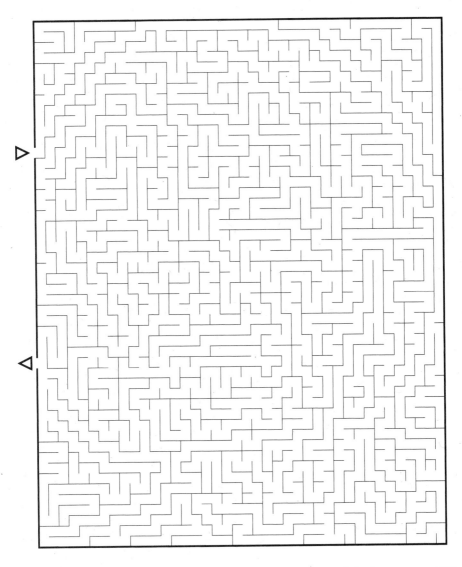

Solution on page 358

R This is a reversed maze. After you have traced the true path (solution) lightly in pencil, color in all the wrong paths with a thick pen or pencil to create your picture.

Solution on page 359

R This is a reversed maze. After you have traced the true path (solution) lightly in pencil, color in all the wrong paths with a thick pen or pencil to create your picture.

Solution on page 359

R This is a reversed maze. After you have traced the true path (solution) lightly in pencil, color in all the wrong paths with a thick pen or pencil to create your picture.

Maze #222

Solution on page 359

R This is a reversed maze. After you have traced the true path (solution) lightly in pencil, color in all the wrong paths with a thick pen or pencil to create your picture.

Maze #223

Solution on page 360

R This is a reversed maze. After you have traced the true path
(solution) lightly in pencil, color in all the wrong paths with a thick
pen or pencil to create your picture.

Solution on page 360

R This is a reversed maze. After you have traced the true path (solution) lightly in pencil, color in all the wrong paths with a thick pen or pencil to create your picture.

Maze #225

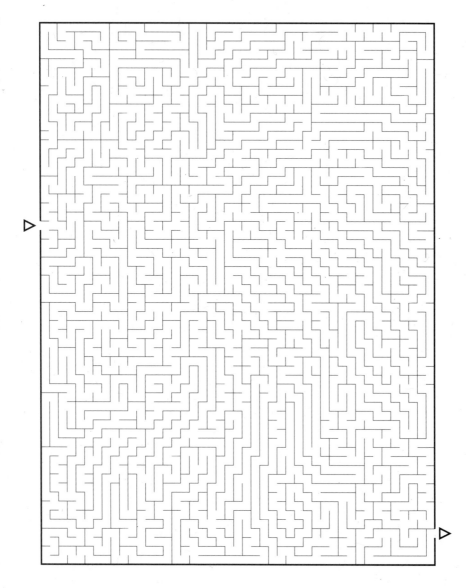

Solution on page 360

R This is a reversed maze. After you have traced the true path (solution) lightly in pencil, color in all the wrong paths with a thick pen or pencil to create your picture.

Solution on page 361

R This is a reversed maze. After you have traced the true path (solution) lightly in pencil, color in all the wrong paths with a thick pen or pencil to create your picture.

Solution on page 361

R This is a reversed maze. After you have traced the true path (solution) lightly in pencil, color in all the wrong paths with a thick pen or pencil to create your picture.

Solution on page 361

R This is a reversed maze. After you have traced the true path (solution) lightly in pencil, color in all the wrong paths with a thick pen or pencil to create your picture.

Solution on page 362

R This is a reversed maze. After you have traced the true path (solution) lightly in pencil, color in all the wrong paths with a thick pen or pencil to create your picture.

Solution on page 362

R This is a reversed maze. After you have traced the true path (solution) lightly in pencil, color in all the wrong paths with a thick pen or pencil to create your picture.

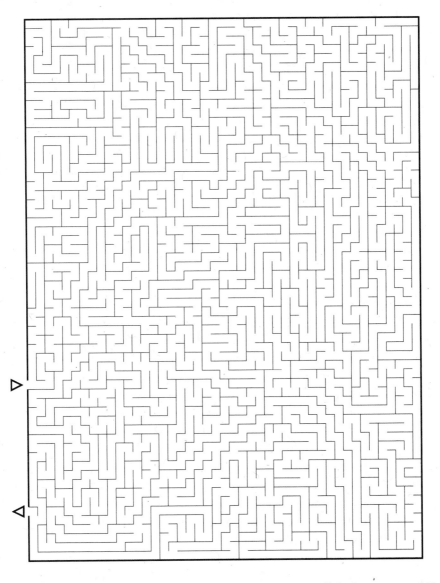

Solution on page 362

R This is a reversed maze. After you have traced the true path (solution) lightly in pencil, color in all the wrong paths with a thick pen or pencil to create your picture.

Maze #232

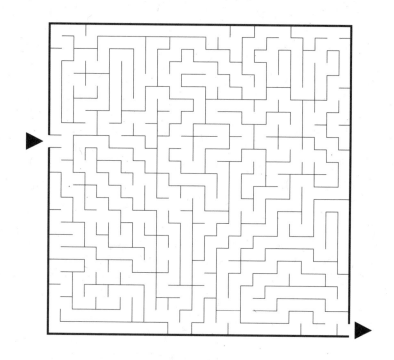

Maze #233

Solutions on page 363

Maze #234

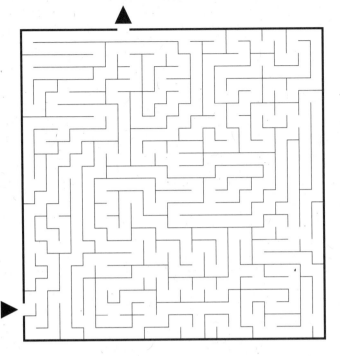

Maze #235

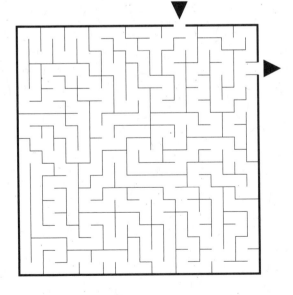

Solutions on page 363

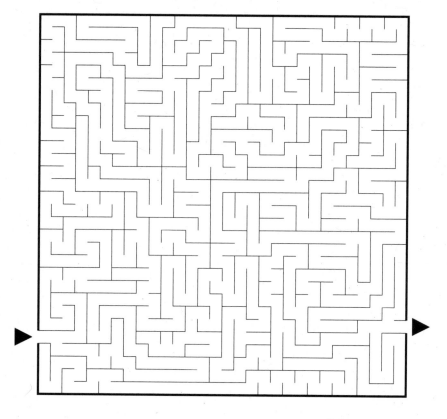

Solution on page 363

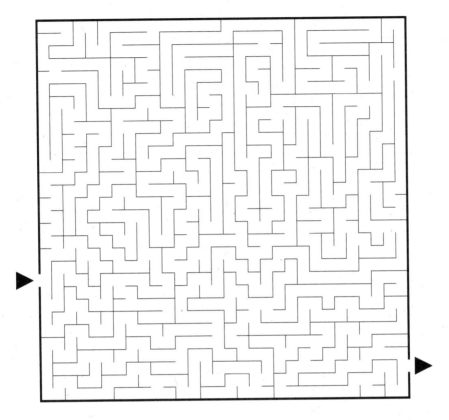

Solution on page 364

Maze #238

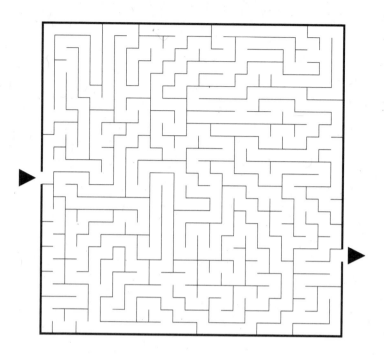

Maze #239

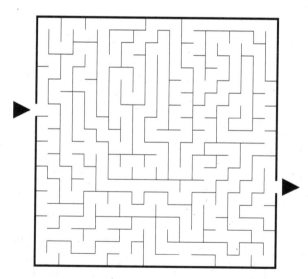

Solutions on page 364

Maze #240

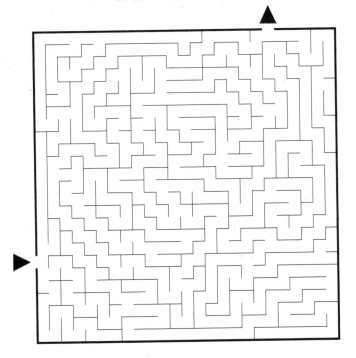

Maze #241

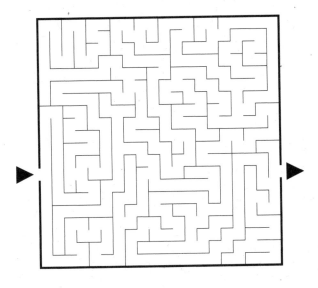

Solutions on page 365

Solution on page 365

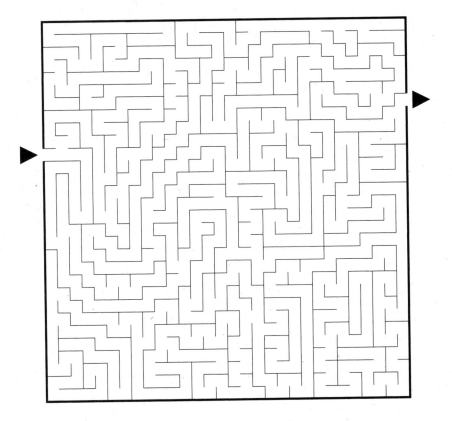

Solution on page 365

Solution on page 366

Maze #245

Solution on page 366

Solution on page 366

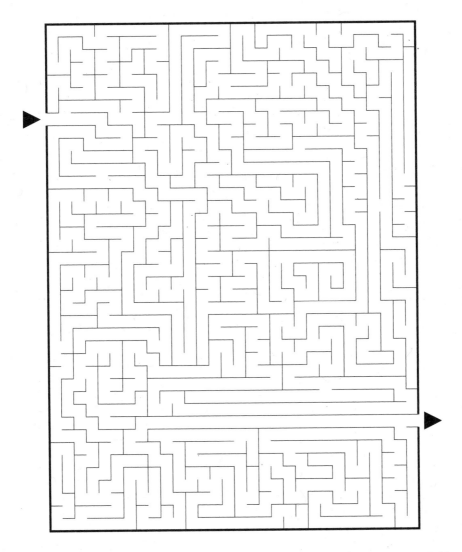

Solution on page 367

Solution on page 367

Solution on page 367

Solution on page 368

Solution on page 368

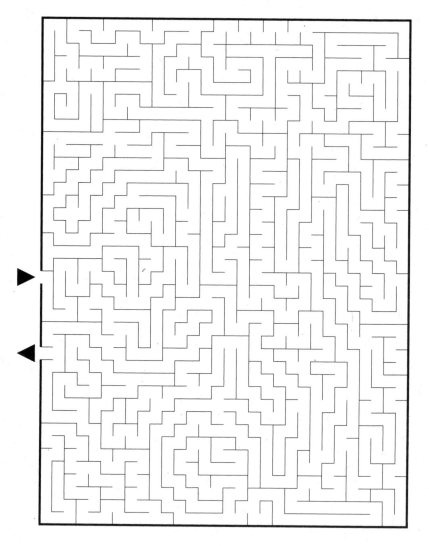

Solution on page 368

Solution on page 369

Solution on page 369

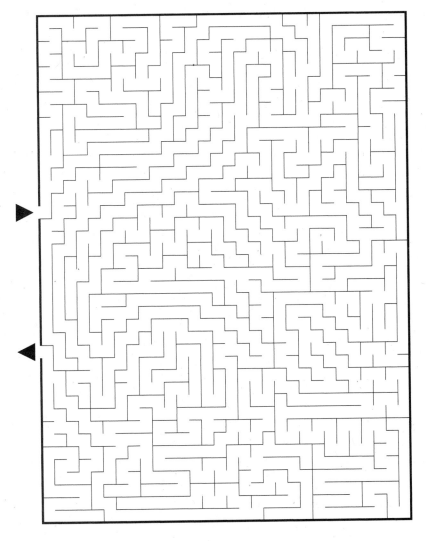

Solution on page 369

Solution on page 370

Solution on page 370

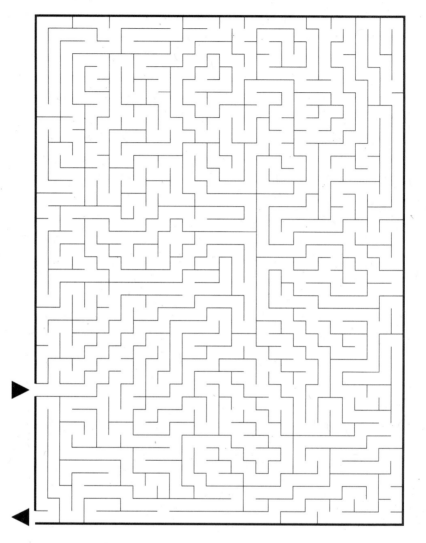

Solution on page 370

Solution on page 371

Solution on page 371

Maze #261

Solution on page 371

Solution on page 372

Solution on page 372

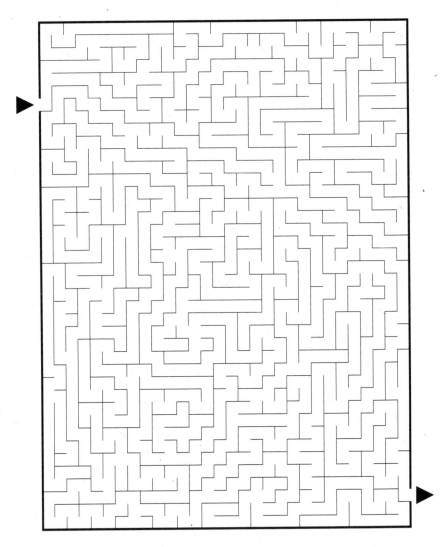

Solution on page 372

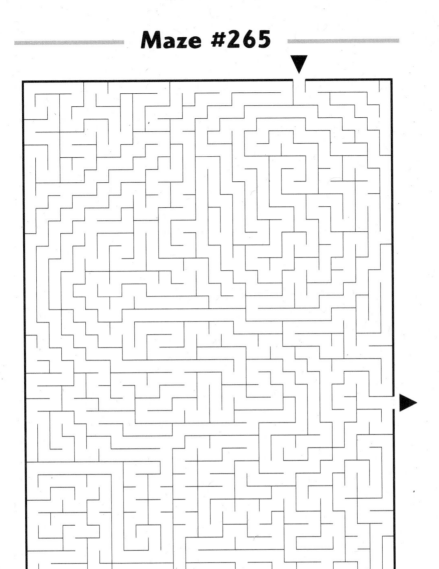

Solution on page 373

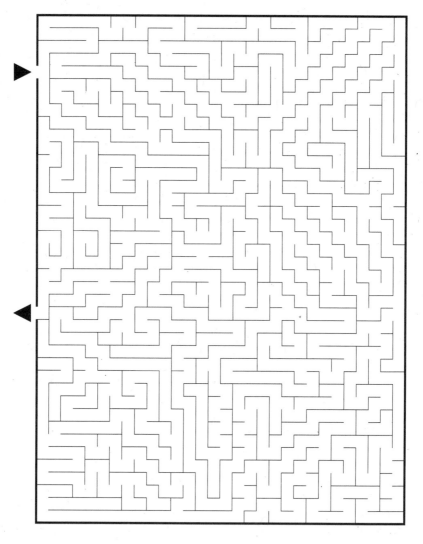

Solution on page 373

Solution on page 373

Maze #268

Solution on page 374

Solution on page 374

Solution on page 374

Solution on page 375

Solution on page 375

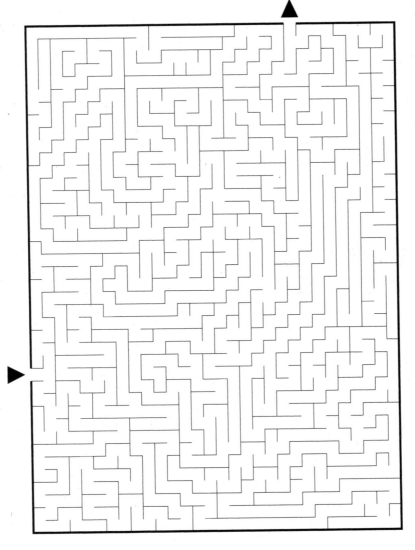

Solution on page 376

Solution on page 376

Maze #277

Solution on page 377

Solution on page 377

Maze #279

Solution on page 377

Solution on page 377

Solution on page 378

Solution on page 378

Maze #283

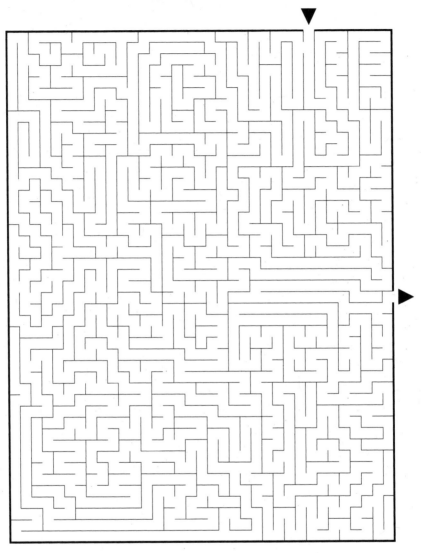

Solution on page 378

Solution on page 378

Solution on page 379

Maze #286

Solution on page 379

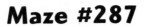

Solution on page 379

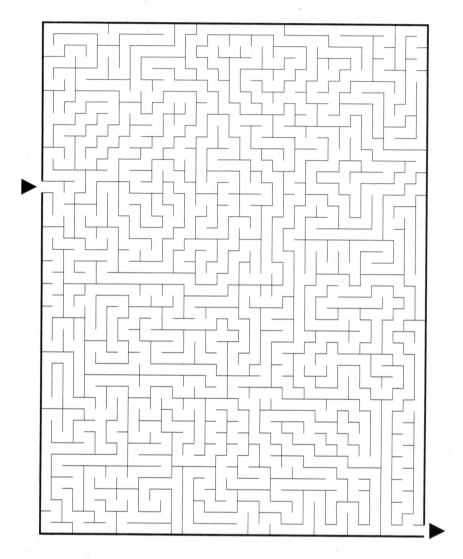

Solution on page 379

Solution on page 380

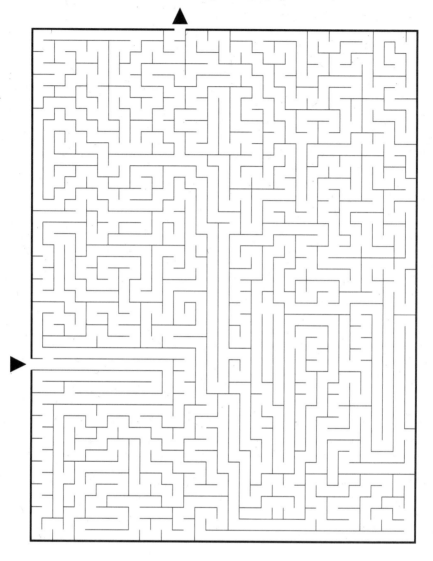

Solution on page 380

Maze #291

Solution on page 380

Solution on page 380

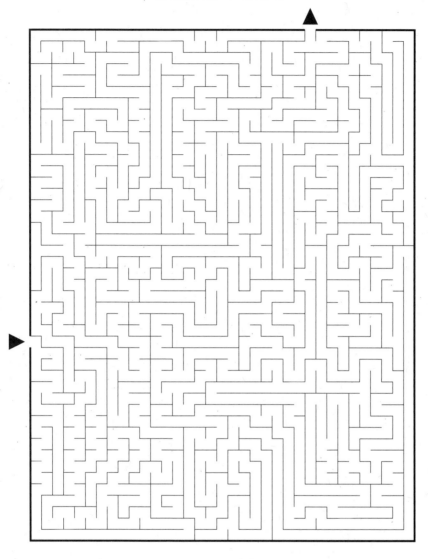

Solution on page 381

Solution on page 381

Solution on page 381

Solution on page 381

Solution on page 382

Solution on page 382

Solution on page 382

Solution on page 382

Maze #301

Solution on page 383

Solution on page 383

Maze #303

Solution on page 383

Solution on page 383

Maze #305

Solution on page 384

Solution on page 384

Solution on page 384

Solution on page 384

SOLUTIONS

Solutions

Maze #1

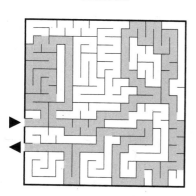

Maze #2

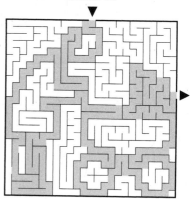

Maze #3

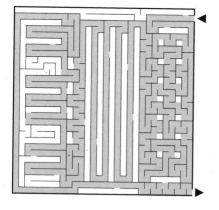

Maze #4

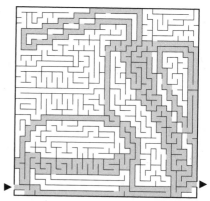

Solutions

Maze #5

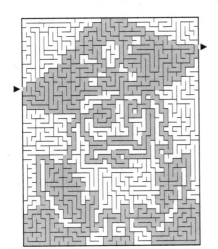

Maze #6

Maze #7

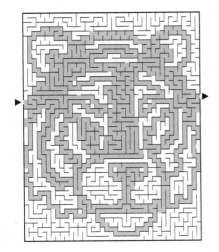

Maze #8

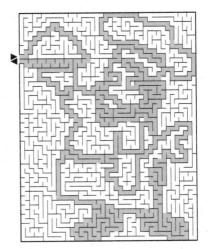

Solutions

Maze #9

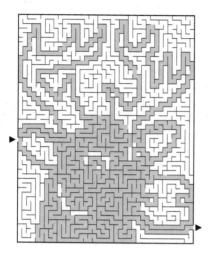

Maze #10

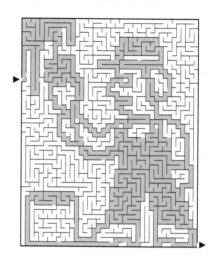

Maze #11

Maze #12

Solutions

Maze #13

Maze #14

Maze #15

Solutions

Maze #16

Maze #17

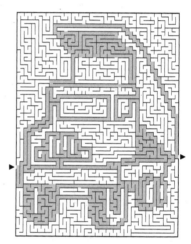

Maze #18

Solutions

Maze #19

Maze #20

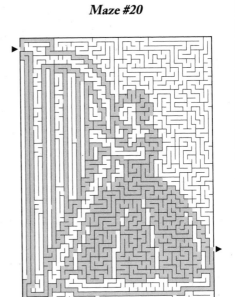

Maze #21

Maze #22

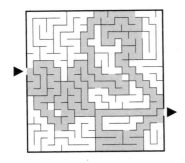

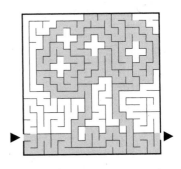

Solutions

Maze #23

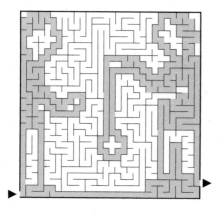

Maze #24

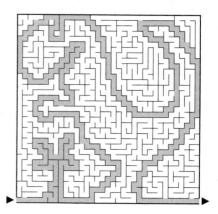

Maze #25

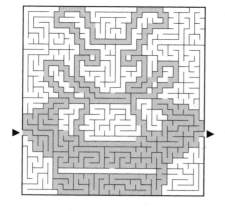

Maze #26

Solutions

Maze #27

Maze #28

Maze #29

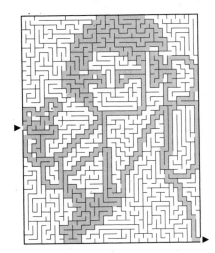

Solutions

Maze #30

Maze #31

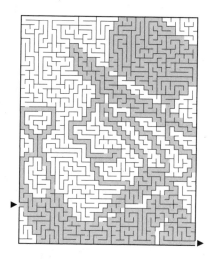

Maze #32

Solutions

Maze #33

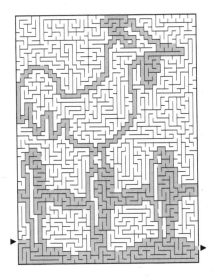

Maze #34

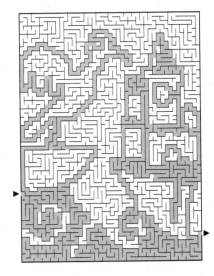

Maze #35

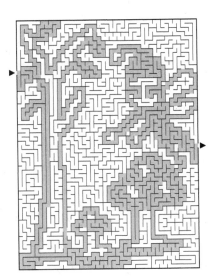

Solutions

Maze #36

Maze #37

Maze #38

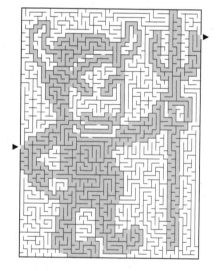

Maze #39

Solutions

Maze #40

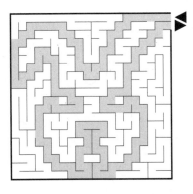

Maze #41

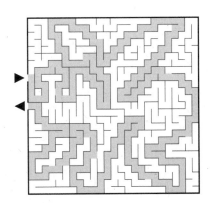

Maze #42

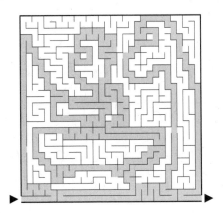

Maze #43

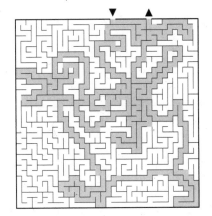

Solutions

Maze #44

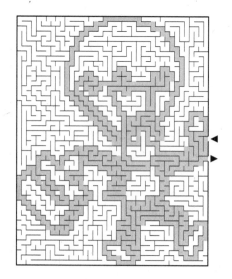

Maze #45

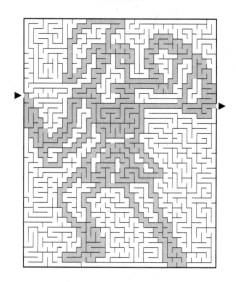

Maze #46

Maze #47

Solutions

Maze #48

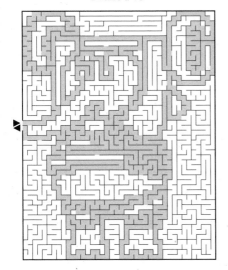

Maze #49

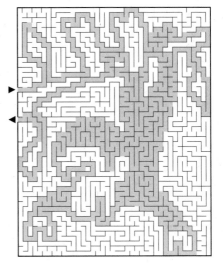

Maze #50

Solutions

Maze #51

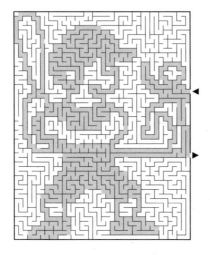

Maze #52

Maze #53

Solutions

Maze #54

Maze #55

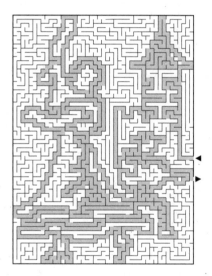

Maze #56

Solutions

Maze #57

Maze #58

Maze #59

Solutions

Maze #60

Maze #61

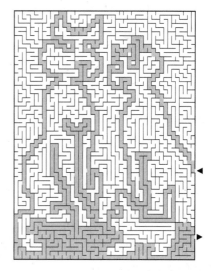

Maze #62

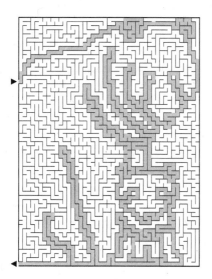

Solutions

Maze #63

Maze #64

Maze #65

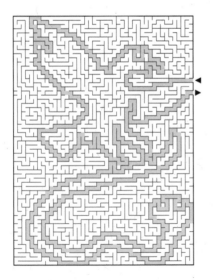

Solutions

Maze #66

Elvis Presley

Maze #67

Socrates

Maze #68

Charlie Chaplin

Solutions

Maze #69

Anne Frank

Maze #70

Babe Ruth

Maze #71

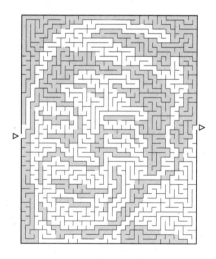

Nelson Mandela

Maze #72

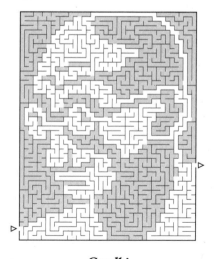

Gandhi

Solutions

Maze #73

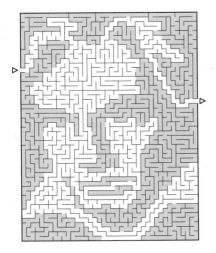

Beethoven

Maze #74

William Shakespeare

Maze #75

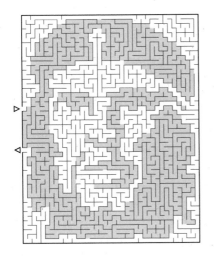

Che Guevera

Maze #76

Maze #77

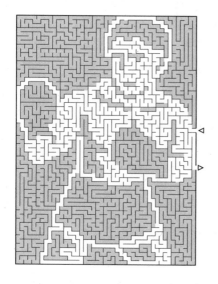

Maze #80

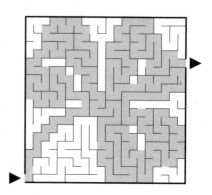

Maze #78

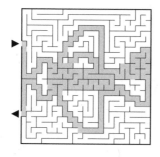

Maze #81

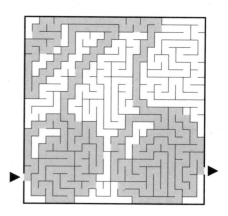

Maze #79

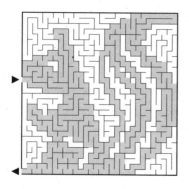

Solutions

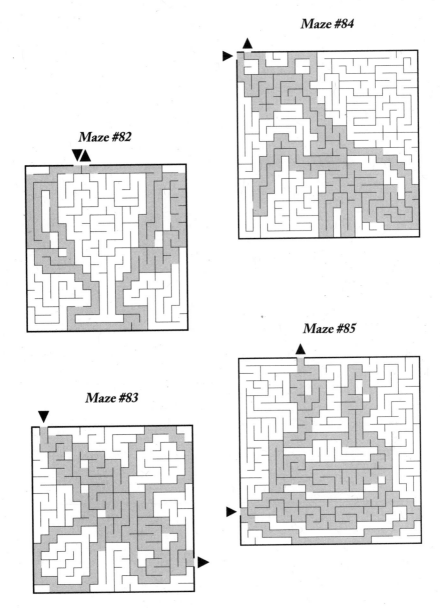

Maze #84

Maze #82

Maze #85

Maze #83

Solutions

Maze #88

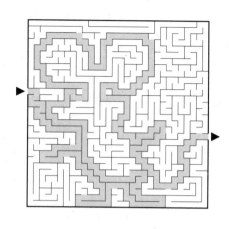

Maze #86

Maze #89

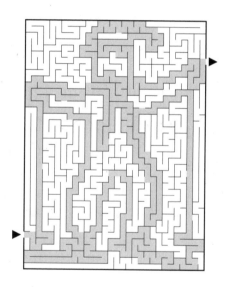

Maze #87

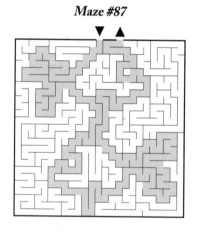

Solutions

Maze #90

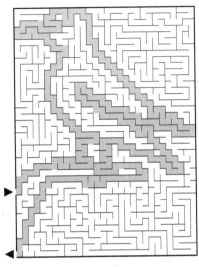

Maze #92

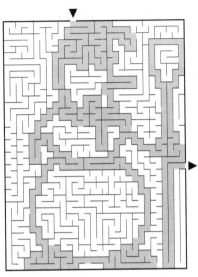

Maze #91

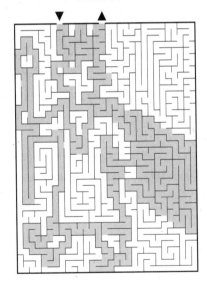

Maze #93

Solutions

Maze #94

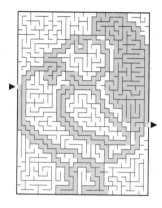

Maze #97

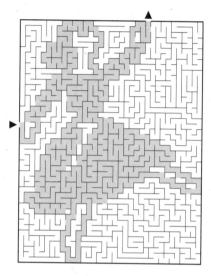

Maze #95

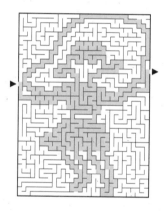

Maze #98

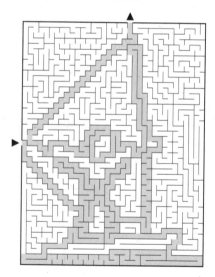

Maze #96

Solutions

Maze #101

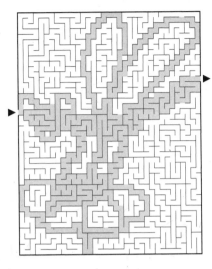

Maze #99

Maze #100

Maze #102

Solutions

Maze #103

Maze #105

Maze #104

Maze #106

Solutions

Maze #109

Maze #107

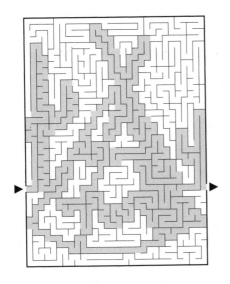

Maze #110

Maze #108

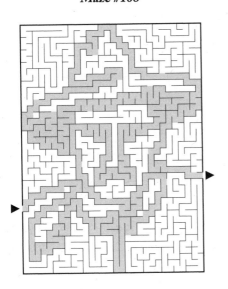

Solutions

Maze #111

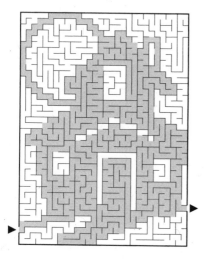

Maze #113

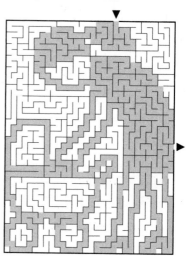

Maze #112

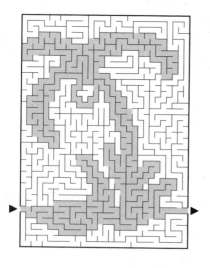

Maze #114

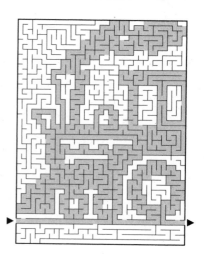

Solutions

Maze #117

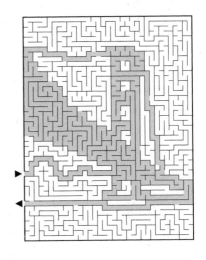

Maze #115

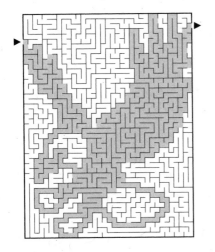

Maze #116

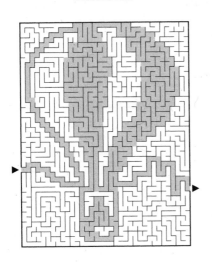

Maze #118

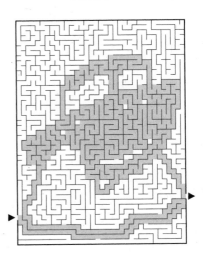

Solutions

Maze #121

Maze #119

Maze #122

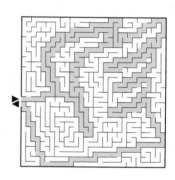

Maze #120

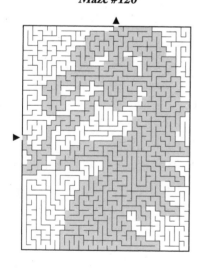

Maze #123

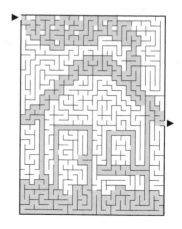

Solutions

Maze #124

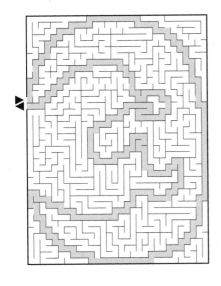

Maze #126

Maze #125

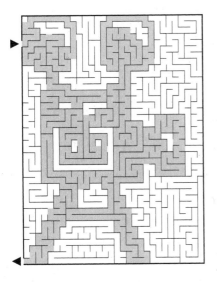

Maze #127

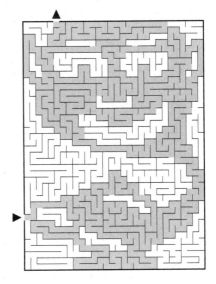

Solutions

Maze #130

Maze #128

Maze #131

Maze #129

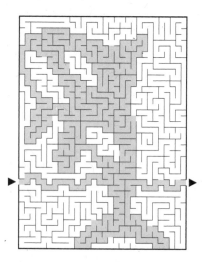

Maze #132

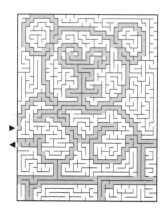

Solutions

Maze #133

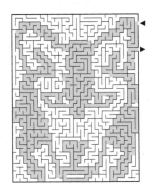

Maze #136

Maze #134

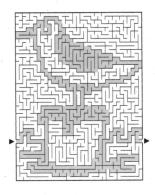

Maze #137

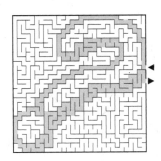

Maze #135

Maze #138

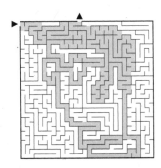

Solutions

Maze #140

Maze #139

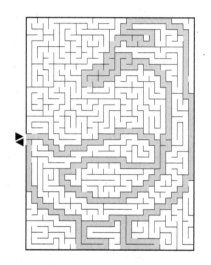

Maze #141

Solutions

Maze #142

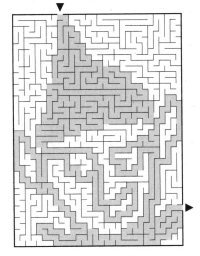

Maze #143

Maze #144

Solutions

Maze #146

Maze #145

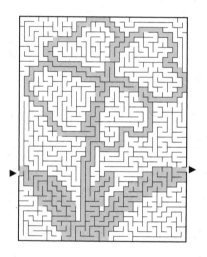

Maze #147

Solutions

Maze #148

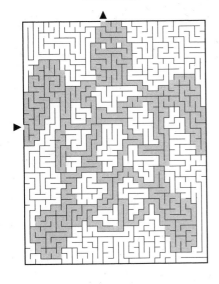

Maze #149

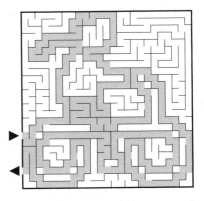

Maze #150

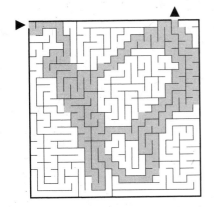

Solutions

Maze #152

Maze #151

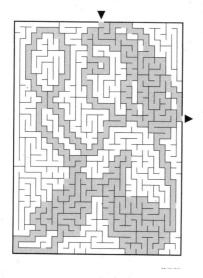

Maze #153

Solutions

Maze #154

Maze #157

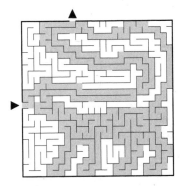

Maze #155

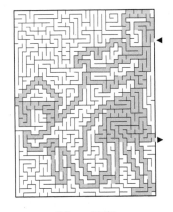

Maze #158

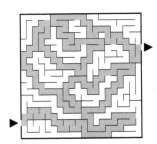

Maze #156

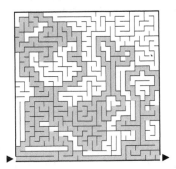

Solutions

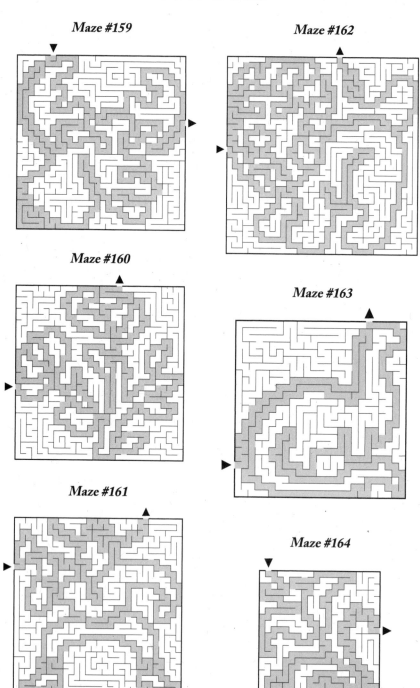

Maze #159

Maze #162

Maze #160

Maze #163

Maze #161

Maze #164

Solutions

Maze #165

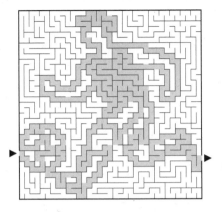

Maze #166

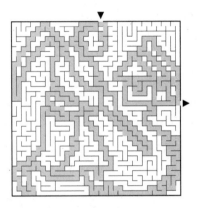

Maze #167

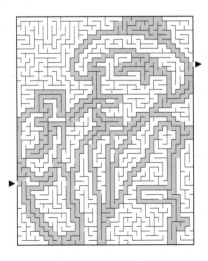

Solutions

Maze #170

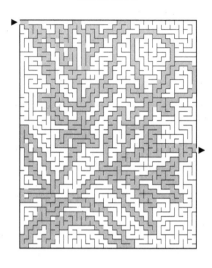

Maze #168

Maze #169

Maze #171

Solutions

Maze #172

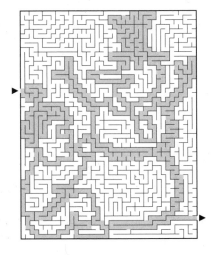

Maze #174

Maze #173

Maze #175

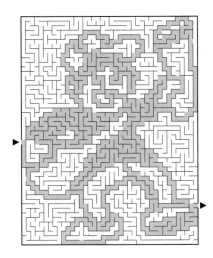

Solutions

Maze #178

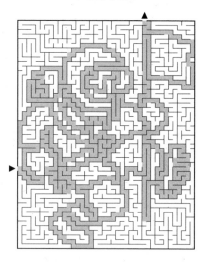

Maze #176

Maze #177

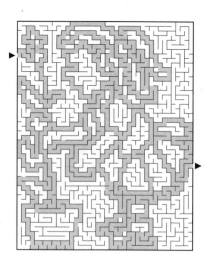

Maze #179

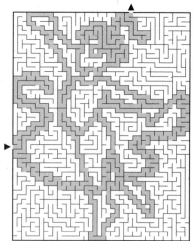

Solutions

Maze #180

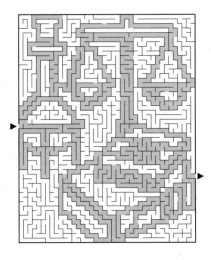

Maze #182

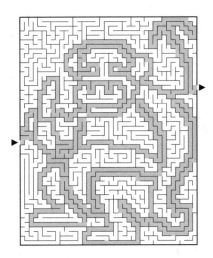

Maze #181

Maze #183

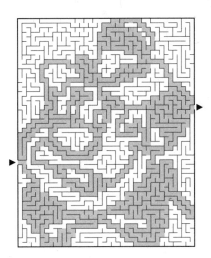

Solutions

Maze #186

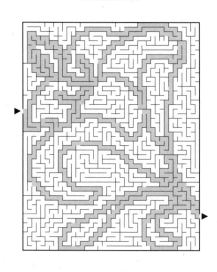

Maze #184

Maze #185

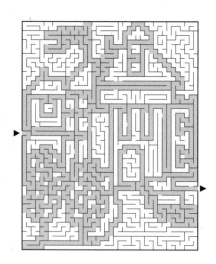

Maze #187

Solutions

Maze #188

Maze #190

Maze #189

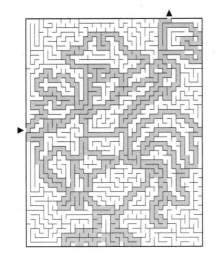

Maze #191

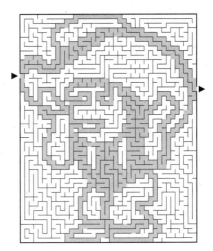

Solutions

Maze #194

Maze #192

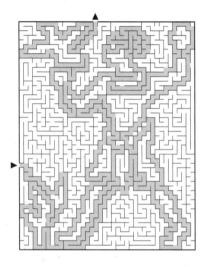

Maze #193

Maze #195

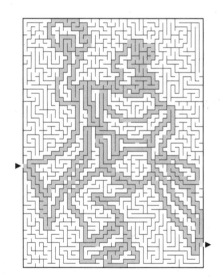

Solutions

Maze #196

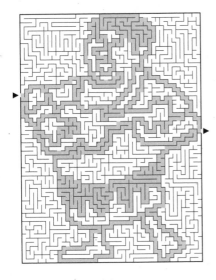

Maze #198

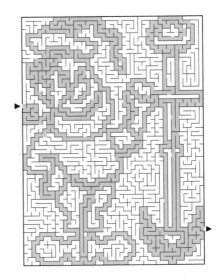

Maze #197

Maze #199

Solutions

Maze #200

Maze #201

Maze #202

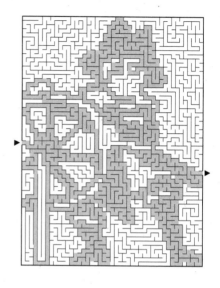

Maze #203

Solutions

Maze #204

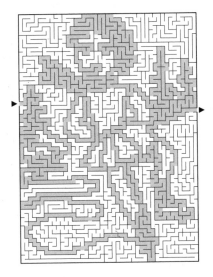

Maze #206

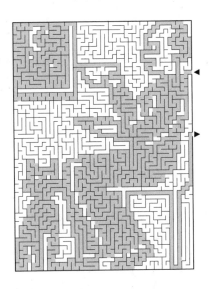

Maze #205

Maze #207

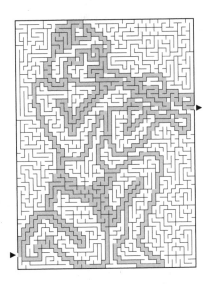

Solutions

id="2" /> Maze #210

Maze #210

Maze #208

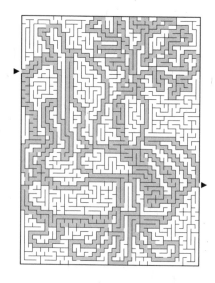

Maze #211

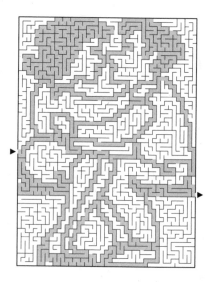

Maze #209

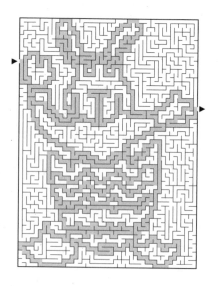

Solutions

Maze #212

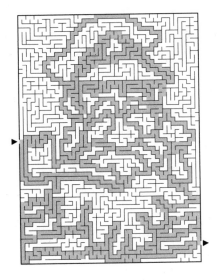

Maze #214

Maze #213

Maze #215

Solutions

Maze #218

Maze #216

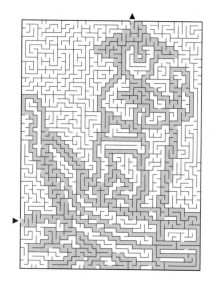

Maze #219

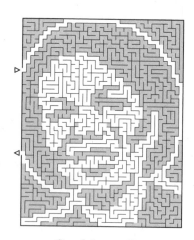

Condoleezza Rice

Maze #217

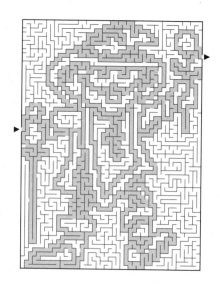

Solutions

Maze #221

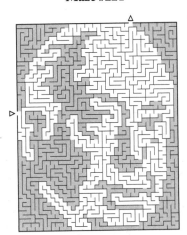

Alfred Hitchcock

Maze #220

Marlon Brando

Maze #222

Eddie Murphy

Solutions

Maze #223

Maze #224

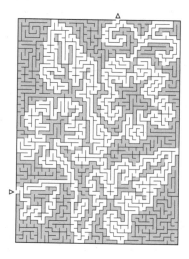

Maze #225

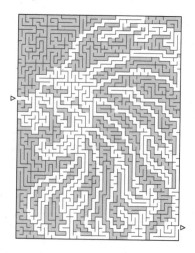

Solutions

Maze #227

Maze #226

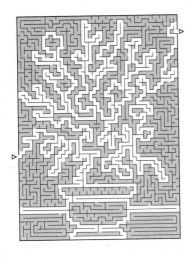

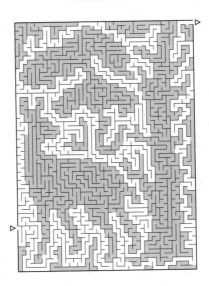

Maze #228

Solutions

Maze #231

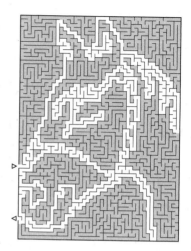

Maze #229

Maze #230

Solutions

Maze #232

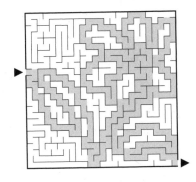

Maze #235

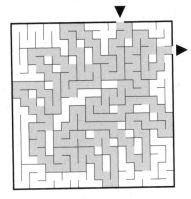

Maze #233

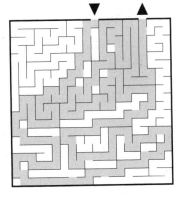

Maze #236

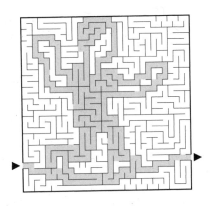

Maze #234

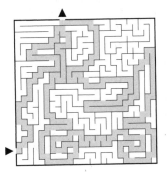

Solutions

Maze #237

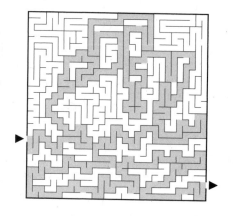

Maze #239

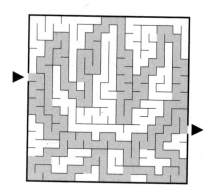

Maze #238

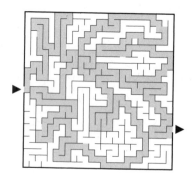

Solutions

Maze #242

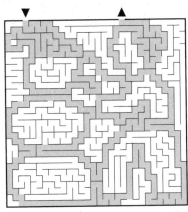

Maze #240

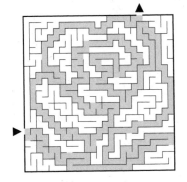

Maze #243

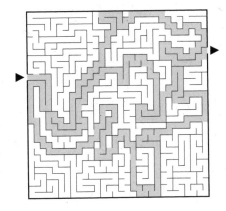

Maze #241

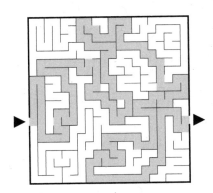

Solutions

Maze #245

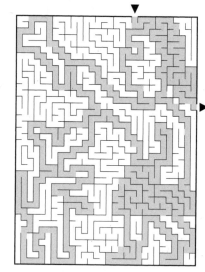

Maze #244

Maze #246

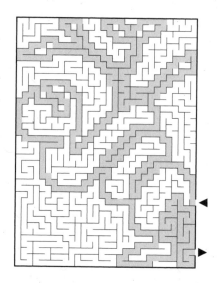

Solutions

Maze #247

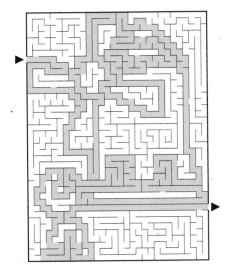

Maze #248

Maze #249

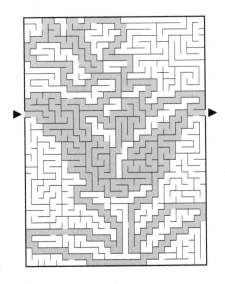

Solutions

Maze #251

Maze #250

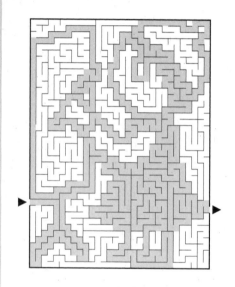

Maze #252

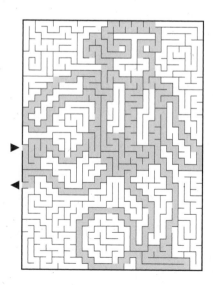

Solutions

Maze #253

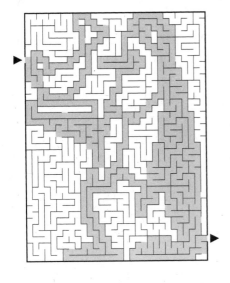

Maze #254

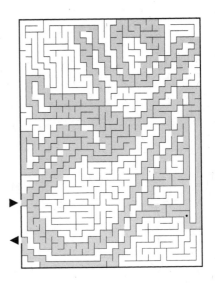

Maze #255

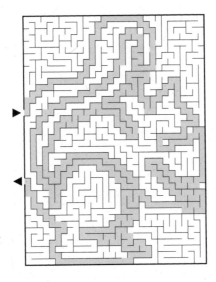

Solutions

Maze #257

Maze #256

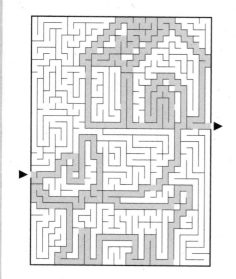

Maze #258

Solutions

Maze #259

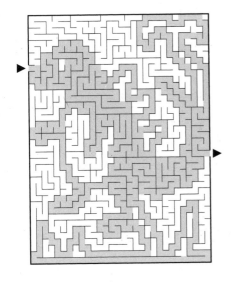

Maze #260

Maze #261

Solutions

Maze #263

Maze #262

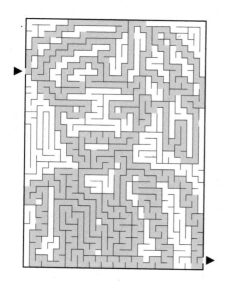

Maze #264

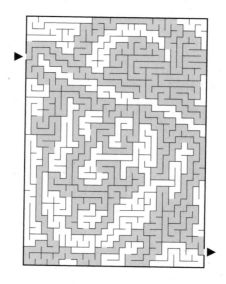

Solutions

Maze #265

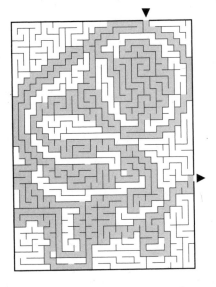

Maze #266

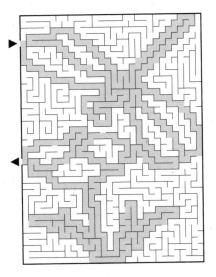

Maze #267

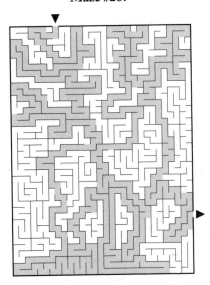

Solutions

Maze #269

Maze #268

Maze #270

Solutions

Maze #277

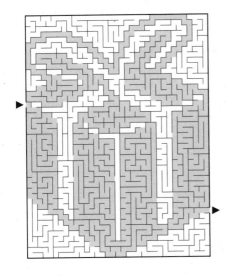

Maze #278

Maze #279

Maze #280

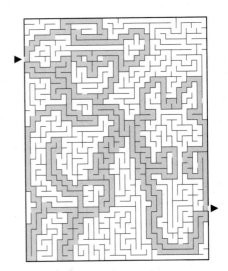

Solutions

Maze #281

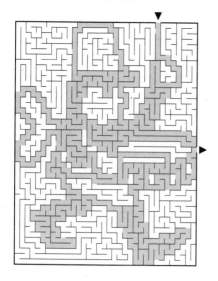

Maze #282

Maze #283

Maze #284

Solutions

Maze #285

Maze #286

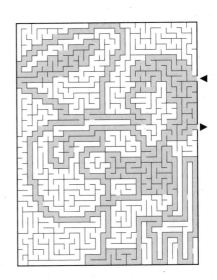

Maze #287

Maze #288

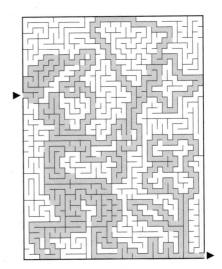

Solutions

Maze #289

Maze #290

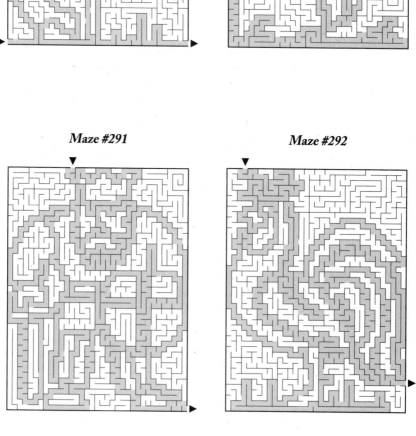

Maze #291

Maze #292

Solutions

Maze #293

Maze #294

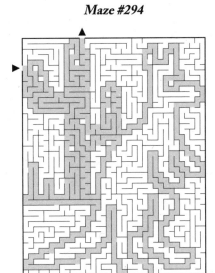

Maze #295

Maze #296

Solutions

Maze #297

Maze #298

Maze #299

Maze #300

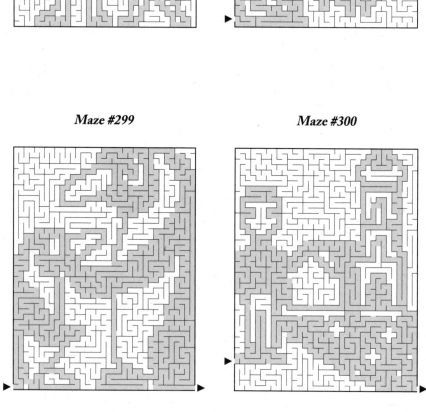

Solutions

Maze #301

Maze #302

Maze #303

Maze #304

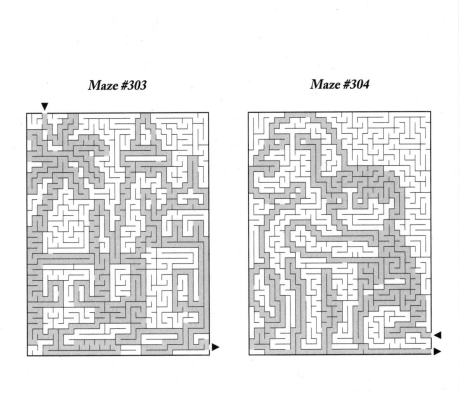

Solutions

Maze #305

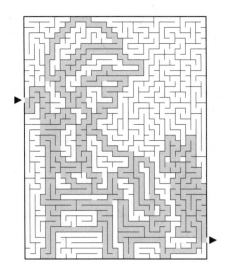

Maze #306

Maze #307

Maze #308